G000153771

The
Supporters'
Guide
to
Non-League
Football
2006

EDITOR
John Robinson

Fourteenth Edition

For details of our range of almost 1,200 books and over 200 DVDs, visit our web site or contact us using the information shown below.

British Library Cataloguing in Publication Data
A catalogue record for this book is available from the British Library

ISBN 1-86223-128-1

Copyright © 2005, SOCCER BOOKS LIMITED (01472 696226)
72 St. Peter's Avenue, Cleethorpes, N.E. Lincolnshire, DN35 8HU, England

Web site   www.soccer-books.co.uk   •   e-mail   info@soccer-books.co.uk

Printed by The Cromwell Press

FOREWORD

Our thanks go to the numerous club officials who have aided us in the compilation of information contained in this guide and also to Michael Robinson (page layouts), Bob Budd (cover artwork) and Tony Brown (Cup Statistics – www.soccerdata.com) for the part they have played.

Although we use the term 'Child' for concessionary prices, this is usually the price charged to Senior Citizens also.

Wherever possible we have included web site information as a new item but, to date, not all clubs have this facility.

Following last year's reorganisation of the Non-League Pyramid structure, we have confined this guide to the 66 Football Conference Clubs in Steps 1 & 2. Our other Non-League guide covering Step 3 level clubs will be published in September 2005 and we would like to wish our readers a happy and safe spectating season.

John Robinson

John Robinson
EDITOR

CONTENTS

The Football Conference National Clubs & Information 5-27

The Football Conference North Clubs & Information 28-50

The Football Conference South Clubs & Information 51-73

2004/2005 Statistics for the Nationwide Conference National 74

2004/2005 Statistics for the Nationwide Conference North 75

2004/2005 Statistics for the Nationwide Conference South 76

2004/2005 Statistics for the Unibond Premier Division 77

2004/2005 Stats. for the Southern Premier League – Premier Division 78

2004/2005 Statistics for the Isthmian Premier Division 79

2004/2005 LDV Trophy Results 80-81

2004/2005 F.A. Trophy Results 82-86

2004/2005 F.A. Vase Results 87-91

2005/2006 Season Fixtures for the Football Conference 92-94

Other Titles 95-96

THE NATIONWIDE FOOTBALL CONFERENCE NATIONAL CLUBS

Address

Riverside House, 14B High Street, Crayford, Kent DA1 4HG

Phone (01322) 411021   **Fax** (01322) 411022

Clubs for the 2005/2006 Season

Accrington Stanley FC .... Page 6
Aldershot Town FC .... Page 7
Altrincham FC .... Page 8
Burton Albion FC .... Page 9
Cambrdige United FC .... Page 10
Canvey Island FC .... Page 11
Crawley Town FC .... Page 12
Dagenham & Redbridge FC .... Page 13
Exeter City FC .... Page 14
Forest Green Rovers FC .... Page 15
Gravesend & Northfleet FC .... Page 16
Grays Athletic FC .... Page 17
Halifax Town FC .... Page 18
Hereford United FC .... Page 19
Kidderminster Harriers FC .... Page 20
Morecambe FC .... Page 21
Scarborough FC .... Page 22
Southport FC .... Page 23
Stevenage Borough FC .... Page 24
Tamworth FC .... Page 25
Woking FC .... Page 26
York City FC .... Page 27

ACCRINGTON STANLEY FC

Founded: 1876 (Reformed 1968)
Former Names: None
Nickname: 'Stanley' 'Reds'
Ground: The Interlink Express Stadium, Livingstone Road, Accrington, Lancashire   BB5 5BX
Record Attendance: 4,368 (3rd January 2004)
Pitch Size: 112 × 72 yards

Colours: Red shirts with White shorts
Telephone N°: (01254) 356950
Fax Number: (01254) 356951
Ground Capacity: 5,050
Seating Capacity: 1,200
Web site: www.accringtonstanley.co.uk

GENERAL INFORMATION

Supporters Club: Malcolm Isherwood, c/o Club
Telephone N°: –
Car Parking: 300 spaces available at the ground
Coach Parking: At the ground
Nearest Railway Station: Accrington (1 mile)
Nearest Bus Station: Accrington Town Centre (1 mile)
Club Shop: At the ground, at Oswaldtwistle Mills Shopping Village and also through the club web site
Opening Times: Weekdays 9.00am – 5.00pm; Saturday matchdays 10.00am – 5.00pm
Telephone N°: (01254) 356954
Police Telephone N°: (01254) 382141

GROUND INFORMATION

Away Supporters' Entrances & Sections:
Signposted on matchdays

ADMISSION INFO (2004/2005 PRICES)

Adult Standing: £12.00
Adult Seating: £12.00
Senior Citizen/Junior Standing: £7.00
Senior Citizen/Junior Seating: £7.00
Under-12s: £3.00
Programme Price: £2.00

DISABLED INFORMATION

Wheelchairs: Specific areas around the ground
Helpers: Admitted
Prices: Standard prices apply
Disabled Toilets: Yes
Contact: (01254) 356950   (Bookings are not necessary)

Travelling Supporters' Information:
Routes: Take the M6 to the M65 signposted for Blackburn/Burnley. Exit at Junction 7 and follow the sign for Padiham. Turn right at first traffic lights then right at next. Follow Whalley Road towards Accrington, go through lights at the Greyhound Inn. Turn left into Livingstone Road, 500 yards past traffic lights (signposted Accrington Stanley). The ground is signposted from Junction 7 of the M65 – follow the brown signs with the white football.

ALDERSHOT TOWN FC

Founded: 1992
Former Names: Aldershot FC
Nickname: 'Shots'
Ground: Recreation Ground, High Street, Aldershot, GU11 1TW
Record Attendance: 7,500 (18/11/2000)
Pitch Size: 117 × 76 yards

Colours: Red shirts, shorts and socks
Telephone N°: (01252) 320211
Fax Number: (01252) 324347
Club Secretary: (01252) 337065 – Andrew Morgan
Ground Capacity: 7,500
Seating Capacity: 1,885
Web site: www.shotsweb.co.uk

GENERAL INFORMATION

Supporters Club: c/o Club
Telephone N°: (01252) 320211
Car Parking: Municipal Car Park is adjacent
Coach Parking: Contact the club for information
Nearest Railway Station: Aldershot (5 mins. walk)
Nearest Bus Station: Aldershot (5 minutes walk)
Club Shop: At the ground
Opening Times: Matchdays only
Telephone N°: (01252) 320211
Police Telephone N°: (01252) 324545

GROUND INFORMATION

Away Supporters' Entrances & Sections:
Accommodation in the East Bank Terrace

ADMISSION INFO (2005/2006 PRICES)

Adult Standing: £12.00
Adult Seating: £15.00
Child Standing: £7.00
Child Seating: £8.00
Senior Citizen Standing: £7.00
Senior Citizen Seating: £8.00
Programme Price: £2.00

DISABLED INFORMATION

Wheelchairs: Accommodated in a covered area
Helpers: Admitted
Prices: Free for the disabled. Helpers charged £4.00
Disabled Toilets: None
Contact: (01252) 320211 (Bookings are necessary)

Travelling Supporters' Information:
Routes: From the M3: Exit at Junction 4 and follow signs for Aldershot (A331). Leave the A331 at the A323 exit (Ash Road) and continue along into the High Street. The ground is just past the Railway Bridge on the right; From the A31: Continue along the A31 to the junction with the A331, then as above; From the A325 (Farnborough Road): Follow signs to the A323 then turn left into Wellington Avenue. The ground is just off the 2nd roundabout on the left – the floodlights are clearly visible.

ALTRINCHAM FC

Founded: 1903
Former Names: None
Nickname: 'The Robins'
Ground: Moss Lane, Altrincham   WA15 8AP
Record Attendance: 10,275 (February 1925)
Pitch Size: 110 × 74 yards

Colours: Red and White striped shirts, Black shorts
Telephone Nº: (0161) 928-1045
Daytime Phone Nº: (0161) 928-1045
Fax Number: (0161) 926-9934
Ground Capacity: 6,085
Seating Capacity: 1,154
Web site: www.altrinchamfc.com

GENERAL INFORMATION
Supporters Trust: Jon Stack, STAR, c/o Club
Telephone Nº: –
Car Parking: Adjacent to the ground
Coach Parking: By Police Direction
Nearest Railway Station: Altrincham (5 minutes walk)
Nearest Bus Station: Altrincham
Club Shop: At the ground
Opening Times: Matchdays only
Telephone Nº: (0161) 928-1045
Police Telephone Nº: (0161) 872-5050

GROUND INFORMATION
Away Supporters' Entrances & Sections:
Richmans End turnstiles and accommodation

ADMISSION INFO (2005/2006 PRICES)
Adult Standing: £10.00
Adult Seating: £12.00
Child Standing: £6.00
Child Seating: £7.00
Under-11s: £2.00
Programme Price: £1.50

DISABLED INFORMATION
Wheelchairs: 3 spaces are available each for home and away fans adjacent to the Away dugout
Helpers: Admitted
Prices: Free for the disabled. £10.00 for helpers
Disabled Toilets: Yes
Contact: (0161) 928-1045   (Bookings are necessary)

Travelling Supporters' Information:
Routes: Exit the M56 at Junction 7, following signs for Hale and Altrincham. Go through the 1st main set of traffic lights and take the 3rd right into Westminster Road and continue into Moss Lane. The ground is on the right.

BURTON ALBION FC

Founded: 1950
Former Names: None
Nickname: 'The Brewers'
Ground: The Pirelli Stadium, Princess Way, Burton-on-Trent DE13 0AR
Record Attendance: 5,860 (at Eton Park in 1964)
Pitch Size: 110 × 72 yards

Colours: Shirts are Yellow with Black trim, shorts are Black with Yellow Trim
Telephone N°: (01283) 565938
Fax Number: (01283) 565938
Ground Capacity: 6,000
Seating Capacity: 2,000
Web site: www.burtonalbionfc.co.uk

GENERAL INFORMATION

Supporters Club: c/o Club
Telephone N°: (01283) 565938
Car Parking: Available on the nearby Rykneld Trading Estate
Coach Parking: Rykneld Trading Estate, Derby Road
Nearest Railway Station: Burton-on-Trent (1½ miles)
Nearest Bus Station: Burton-on-Trent (1½ miles)
Club Shop: At the ground
Opening Times: Weekdays 9.00am – 5.00pm and Matchdays from 1½ hours before kick-off
Telephone N°: (01283) 565938
Police Telephone N°: (08543) 302010

GROUND INFORMATION

Away Supporters' Entrances & Sections:
East Stand, Derby Road

ADMISSION INFO (2005/2006 PRICES)

Adult Standing: £12.00
Adult Seating: £14.00
Child Standing: £3.00
Child Seating: £5.00
Senior Citizen Standing: £10.00
Senior Citizen Seating: £12.00
Programme Price: £2.00

DISABLED INFORMATION

Wheelchairs: Over 78 spaces available for home and away fans in the designated disabled areas
Helpers: Admitted
Prices: Normal prices for the disabled. Free for helpers
Disabled Toilets: Available in all stands
Contact: (01283) 565938 (Bookings are necessary)

Travelling Supporters' Information:
Routes: From the M1, North and South: Exit at Junction 23A and join the A50 towards Derby (also signposted for Alton Towers). Join the A38 southbound at the Toyota factory (towards Burton & Lichfield) then exit for Burton North onto the A5121. Continue past the Pirelli factory on the right and the BP Garage and Cash & Carry on the left then turn into Princess Way at the roundabout; From the M5/6 South: Join the M42 northbound and exit onto the A446 signposted Lichfield. Follow signs for the A38 to Burton then exit onto A5121 as above; From the M6 North: Exit at Junction 15 and follow the A50 towards Stoke and Uttoxeter. Exit the A50 for the A38 southbound signposted Burton and Lichfield at the Toyota factory, then as above.

CAMBRIDGE UNITED FC

Founded: 1912
Former Name: Abbey United FC (1912-1951)
Nickname: 'U's' 'United'
Ground: Abbey Stadium, Newmarket Road,
Cambridge CB5 8LN
Ground Capacity: 8,696
Seating Capacity: 4,376

Pitch Size: 110 × 72 yards
Record Attendance: 14,000 (1/5/70)
Colours: Amber shirts, Black shorts
Telephone Nº: (01223) 566500
Ticket Office: (01223) 566500
Fax Number: (01223) 566502
Web Site: www.cambridgeunited.com

GENERAL INFORMATION

Car Parking: –
Coach Parking: Coldhams Road
Nearest Railway Station: Cambridge (2 miles)
Nearest Bus Station: Cambridge City Centre
Club Shop: At the ground
Opening Times: Monday to Friday 9.00am to 5.00pm and
Matchdays 11.00am to kick-off
Telephone Nº: (01223) 566500
Police Telephone Nº: (01223) 358966

GROUND INFORMATION

Away Supporters' Entrances & Sections:
Coldham Common turnstiles 20-22 – Habbin Terrace (South)
and South Stand (Seating) turnstiles 23-26

ADMISSION INFO (2005/2006 PRICES)

Adult Standing: £12.00
Adult Seating: £15.00
Child Standing: £3.00
Child Seating: £3.00 (in the Family Stand) or £7.00
Concessionary Standing: £8.00
Concessionary Seating: £10.00
Programme Price: £2.50

DISABLED INFORMATION

Wheelchairs: 19 spaces in total for Home fans in the
disabled sections, in front of Main Stand and in the North
Terrace. 16 spaces for Away fans in the South Stand.
Helpers: One helper admitted per disabled fan
Prices: £8.00 for the disabled. Free of charge for helpers
Disabled Toilets: At the rear of the disabled section
Contact: (01223) 566500   (Bookings are necessary)

Travelling Supporters' Information: Routes: From the North: Take the A1 and A14 to Cambridge and then head towards Newmarket. Turn off onto the B1047, signposted for Cambridge Airport, Horningsea and Fen Ditton. Turn right at the top of the slip road and travel through Fen Ditton. Turn right at the traffic lights at the end of the village. Go straight on at the roundabout onto Newmarket Road. The ground is 500 yards on the left; From the South and East: Take the A10 or A130 to the M11. Head North to the A14. Then as from the North; From the West: Take the A422 to Cambridge and join the A14. Then as from North.
Bus Services: Services from the Railway Station to the City Centre and Nº 3 from the City Centre to the Ground.

CANVEY ISLAND FC

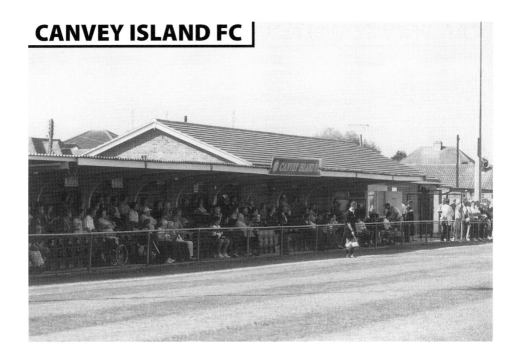

Founded: 1926
Former Names: None
Nickname: 'Gulls'
Ground: Park Lane, Canvey Island, Essex SS8 7PX
Record Attendance: 3,553 (15th April 2003)
Pitch Size: 110 × 80 yards
Colours: Yellow shirts with White shorts

Telephone Nº: (01268) 682991 (Ground)
Daytime Nº: (01268) 511888 (Secretary)
Fax Number: (01268) 511556
Ground Capacity: 4,000
Seating Capacity: 500
Web site: www.canveyislandfc.com

GENERAL INFORMATION
Supporters Club: Mr Chris Gardner, c/o Club
Telephone Nº: (01268) 682991
Car Parking: 80 spaces available at the ground
Coach Parking: At the ground as required
Nearest Railway Station: South Benfleet (2 miles)
Nearest Bus Station: None
Club Shop: At the ground
Opening Times: Matchdays only
Telephone Nº: (01268) 682991
Police Telephone Nº: (01268) 511212

GROUND INFORMATION
Away Supporters' Entrances & Sections:
Segregation only used when there is a large away support

ADMISSION INFO (2005/2006 PRICES)
Adult Standing: £11.50
Adult Seating: £13.50
Student/Senior Citizen Standing: £8.50
Student/Senior Citizen Seating: £10.50
Under 16's Standing: £5.50
Under 16's Seating: £7.50
Programme Price: £2.00

DISABLED INFORMATION
Wheelchairs: Accommodated
Helpers: Admitted
Prices: Concessionary prices apply for the disabled
Disabled Toilets: None
Contact: (01268) 511888 (Bookings are necessary)

Travelling Supporters' Information:
Routes: Take the M25 to either the A127 or the A13 (recommended) then follow the A13 towards Basildon and Southend. At the multiple roundabout system, follow signs for Canvey Island on the A130 towards the Town Centre. Keep to the left hand lane through the one-way system for approximately 1½ miles. Continue past the old bus garage and Park Lane is the first turning on the right.

CRAWLEY TOWN FC

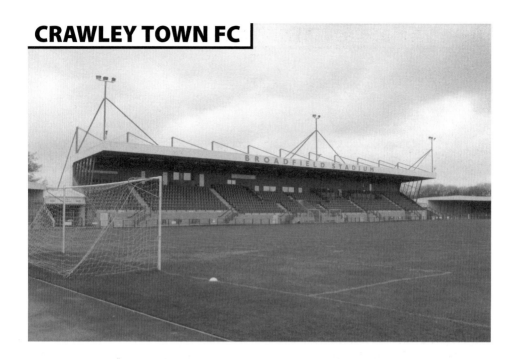

Founded: 1896
Former Names: None
Nickname: 'Red Devils'
Ground: Broadfield Stadium, Brighton Road, Crawley, Sussex   RH11 9RX
Record Attendance: 4,516 (2004)
Pitch Size: 110 × 72 yards

Colours: Red shirts and shorts
Telephone N°: (01293) 410000 (Ground)
Daytime N°: (01293) 410000
Fax Number: (01293) 410002
Ground Capacity: 4,941
Seating Capacity: 1,150
Web site: www.crawley-town-fc.com

GENERAL INFORMATION

Supporters Club: Alain Harper, 33 Nuthurst Close, Ifield, Crawley, Sussex
Telephone N°: (01293) 511764
Car Parking: 350 spaces available at the ground
Coach Parking: At the ground
Nearest Railway Station: Crawley (1 mile)
Nearest Bus Station: By the Railway Station
Club Shop: At the ground
Opening Times: Weekdays and matchdays 9.00am–5.00pm
Telephone N°: (01293) 410000
Police Telephone N°: (08456) 070999

GROUND INFORMATION

Away Supporters' Entrances & Sections:
No usual segregation

ADMISSION INFO (2005/2006 PRICES)

Adult Standing: £11.00
Adult Seating: £13.00
Concessionary Standing: £7.00
Concessionary Seating: £9.00
Junior Reds: £4.00 Seating; Standing is free of charge
Programme Price: £2.00

DISABLED INFORMATION

Wheelchairs: Accommodated in the disabled section of the Main Stand (Lift access available)
Helpers: One helper admitted per disabled fan
Prices: Normal prices apply
Disabled Toilets: Available
Contact: (01293) 410000   (Bookings are not necessary)

Travelling Supporters' Information:
Routes: Exit the M23 at Junction 11 and take the A23 towards Crawley. After ¼ mile, the Stadium is on the left. Take the first exit at the roundabout for the Stadium entrance.

DAGENHAM & REDBRIDGE FC

Founded: 1992
Former Names: Formed by the merger of Dagenham FC and Redbridge Forest FC
Nickname: 'The Daggers'
Ground: Glyn Hopkin Stadium, Victoria Road, Dagenham, Essex   RM10 7XL
Record Attendance: 7,100 (1967)
Pitch Size: 110 × 65 yards

Colours: Red and White shirts with White shorts
Telephone N°: (0208) 592-1549
Office Phone N°: (0208) 592-7194
Secretary's Phone N°: (0208) 592-7194
Fax Number: (0208) 593-7227
Ground Capacity: 6,077
Seating Capacity: 1,015
Web site: www.daggers.co.uk

GENERAL INFORMATION

Supporters Club: Russell Elmes, 24 Brewood, Dagenham, RM8 2BL
Telephone N°: (0208) 593-2801
Car Parking: Street parking only
Coach Parking: Street parking only
Nearest Railway Station: Dagenham East (5 mins. walk)
Nearest Bus Station: Romford
Club Shop: At the ground
Opening Times: Matchdays only
Telephone N°: (0208) 592-7194
Police Telephone N°: (0208) 593-8232

GROUND INFORMATION

Away Supporters' Entrances & Sections:
Pondfield Road entrances for Pondfield Road End

ADMISSION INFO (2005/2006 PRICES)

Adult Standing: £10.00
Adult Seating: £13.00
Under-16s Standing: £5.00
Child Seating: £13.00 (£6.00 in the Family Stand)
Senior Citizen Seating: £6.50 in the Family Stand
Family Tickets: £20.00 – 2 adults + 1 children (Family Stand)
Programme Price: £2.50

DISABLED INFORMATION

Wheelchairs: Accommodated in front of new Stand
Helpers: Admitted
Prices: £5.00 for the disabled. Free of charge for Helpers
Disabled Toilets: Available at the East and West ends of the ground and also in the Clubhouse
Contact: (0208) 592-7194   (Bookings are necessary)

Travelling Supporters' Information:
Routes: From the North & West: Take the M11 to its end and join the A406 South. At the large roundabout take the slip road on the left signposted A13 to Dagenham. As you approach Dagenham, stay in the left lane and follow signs for A1306 signposted Dagenham East. Turn left onto the A1112 at the 3rd set of traffic lights by the McDonalds. Proceed along Ballards Road to The Bull roundabout and bear left. Victoria Road is 450 yards on the left after passing Dagenham East tube station; From the South & East: Follow signs for the A13 to Dagenham. Take the next slip road off signposted Elm Park & Dagenham East then turn right at the roundabout. Go straight on at the next roundabout and turn left onto A1306. After ½ mile you will see a McDonalds on the right. Get into the right hand filter lane and turn right onto A1112. Then as from the North & West.

EXETER CITY FC

Founded: 1904
Former Names: Formed by the amalgamation of St. Sidwell United FC & Exeter United FC
Nickname: 'Grecians'
Ground: St. James Park, Exeter, EX4 6PX
Ground Capacity: 8,977
Seating Capacity: 3,806
Record Attendance: 20,984 (4/3/31)

Pitch Size: 113 × 71 yards
Colours: Red and White striped shirts, Black shorts
Telephone Nº: (01392) 411243
Ticket Office: (01392) 411243
Fax Number: (01392) 413959
Web Site: www.exetercityfc.co.uk

GENERAL INFORMATION

Car Parking: King William Street
Coach Parking: Paris Street Bus Station
Nearest Railway Station: Exeter St. James Park (adjacent)
Nearest Bus Station: Paris Street Bus Station
Club Shop: At the ground
Opening Times: Weekdays 10.00am to 4.00pm; Matchdays from 10.00am until kick-off
Telephone Nº: (01392) 411243
Police Telephone Nº: (0990) 700400

GROUND INFORMATION

Away Supporters' Entrances & Sections:
St. James Road turnstiles for standing in the St. James Road End or Well Street for seating in the Echo & Express Stand

ADMISSION INFO (2005/2006 PRICES)

Adult Standing: £11.00
Adult Seating: £11.00 – £14.00
Senior Citizen/Child Standing: £6.00
Senior Citizen/Child Seating: £6.00 – £8.50
Programme Price: £2.50

DISABLED INFORMATION

Wheelchairs: Accommodated in the Doble Stand and Cliff Bastin Stand
Helpers: One helper admitted per wheelchair
Prices: Free of charge for disabled. Normal prices for helpers
Disabled Toilets: Available by the Cliff Bastin Stand
Contact: (01392) 411243   (Bookings are necessary)

Travelling Supporters' Information:
Routes: From the North: Exit the M5 at Junction 30 and follow signs to the City Centre along Sidmouth Road and onto Heavitree Road. Take the 4th exit at the roundabout into Western Way and the 2nd exit into Tiverton Road then next left into St. James Road; From the East: Take the A30 into Heavitree Road (then as from the North); From the South & West: Take the A38 and follow City Centre signs into Western Way, then take the third exit at the roundabout into St. James Road.
Note: This ground is very difficult to find being in a residential area on the side of a hill without prominent floodlights.

FOREST GREEN ROVERS FC

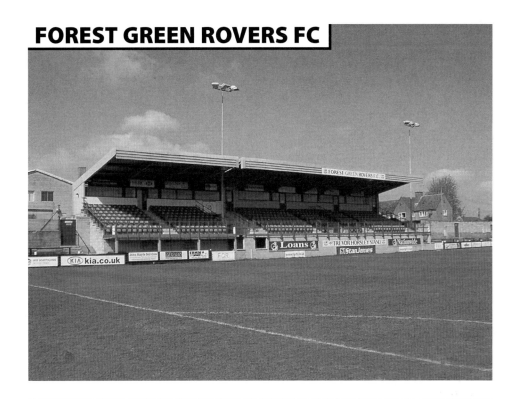

Founded: 1890
Former Names: Stroud FC
Nickname: 'The Rovers'
Ground: The Lawn, Nympsfield Road, Forest Green, Nailsworth, Gloucestershire GL6 0ET
Record Attendance: 3,002 (18/4/99)
Pitch Size: 110 × 70 yards

Colours: Black and White striped shirts, Black shorts
Telephone Nº: (01453) 834860
Fax Number: (01453) 835291
Ground Capacity: 5,141
Seating Capacity: 526
Web site: www.fgrfc.co.uk

GENERAL INFORMATION
Supporters Club: Andrew Whiting, c/o Club
Telephone Nº: (07979) 635087
Car Parking: At the ground
Coach Parking: At the ground
Nearest Railway Station: Stroud
Nearest Bus Station: Nailsworth
Club Shop: At the ground
Opening Times: Matchdays only
Telephone Nº: (07979) 635087
Police Telephone Nº: (01452) 521201

GROUND INFORMATION
Away Supporters' Entrances & Sections:
No usual segregation

ADMISSION INFO (2005/2006 PRICES)
Adult Standing: £9.00
Adult Seating: £11.00
Senior Citizen Standing: £5.50
Senior Citizen Seating: £7.00
Children under 15 Standing: £5.50
Children under 15 Seating: £6.00
Junior Greens: £2.00 – £3.00
Programme Price: £2.50

DISABLED INFORMATION
Wheelchairs: Accommodated in the Main Stand
Helpers: Admitted
Prices: Normal prices for the disabled. Free for helpers
Disabled Toilets: Yes
Contact: (01453) 834860 (Bookings necessary at least 72 hours in advance)

Travelling Supporters' Information:
Routes: The ground is located 4 miles south of Stroud on the A46 to Bath. Upon entering Nailsworth, turn into Spring Hill at the mini-roundabout and the ground is approximately ½ mile up the hill on the left.

GRAVESEND & NORTHFLEET FC

Founded: 1946
Former Names: Formed by the amalgamation of Gravesend United FC & Northfleet United FC
Nickname: 'The Fleet'
Ground: Stonebridge Road, Northfleet, Gravesend, Kent   DA11 9GN
Record Attendance: 12,063 (1963)

Colours: Reds shirts with White shorts
Telephone Nº: (01474) 533796
Fax Number: (01474) 324754
Pitch Size: 112 × 72 yards
Ground Capacity: 4,200
Seating Capacity: 600
Web site: www.gnfc.co.uk

GENERAL INFORMATION
Supporters Club: c/o Club
Telephone Nº: (01474) 533796
Car Parking: Street parking only
Coach Parking: At the ground
Nearest Railway Station: Northfleet (5 minutes walk)
Nearest Bus Station: Bus Stop outside the ground
Club Shop: At the ground
Opening Times: Matchdays only
Telephone Nº: (01474) 533796
Police Telephone Nº: (01474) 564346

GROUND INFORMATION
Away Supporters' Entrances & Sections:
Only some games are segregated – contact club for details

ADMISSION INFO (2005/2006 PRICES)
Adult Standing: £12.00
Adult Seating: £14.00
Senior Citizen/Child Standing: £6.00
Senior Citizen/Child Seating: £7.00
Programme Price: £2.50

DISABLED INFORMATION
Wheelchairs: 6 spaces are available in the Disabled Area in front of the Main Stand
Helpers: Admitted
Prices: Please phone the club for information
Disabled Toilets: Available in the Main Stand
Contact: (01474) 533796   (Bookings are necessary)

Travelling Supporters' Information:
Routes: Take the A2 to the Northfleet/Southfleet exit along the B262 to Northfleet then the B2175 (Springhead Road) to the junction with the A226. Turn left (The Hill, Northfleet) and follow the road (Stonebridge Road). The ground is 1 mile on the right at the foot of the steep hill.

GRAYS ATHLETIC FC

Founded: 1890
Former Names: None
Nickname: 'The Blues'
Ground: The New Recreation Ground, Bridge Road, Grays, Essex RM17 6BZ
Record Attendance: 9,500 (1959)
Pitch Size: 110 × 71 yards

Colours: Sky Blue shirts and shorts
Telephone Nº: (01375) 377753 (Club)
Daytime Telephone Nº: (01375) 391649 (Office)
Fax Number: (01375) 377753
Ground Capacity: 3,333
Seating Capacity: 900
Web site: www.graysathletic.co.uk

GENERAL INFORMATION

Supporters Club: None
Telephone Nº: –
Car Parking: Town Centre Car Parks close to the ground
Coach Parking: Car Parks close to the ground
Nearest Railway Station: Grays
Nearest Bus Station: Grays
Club Shop: At the ground
Opening Times: Matchdays only
Telephone Nº: (01375) 377753
Police Telephone Nº: (01375) 391212

GROUND INFORMATION

Away Supporters' Entrances & Sections:
Bradbourne Road entrances and accommodation

ADMISSION INFO (2005/2006 PRICES)

Adult Standing: £10.00
Adult Seating: £12.00
Concessionary Standing: £6.00
Concessionary Seating: £8.00
Under-11s admitted for £2.00 if accompanied by a paying adult
Programme Price: £2.00

DISABLED INFORMATION

Wheelchairs: Accommodated in the Main Stand
Helpers: Admitted
Prices: Please phone the club for information
Disabled Toilets: One available
Contact: (01375) 391649

Travelling Supporters' Information:
Routes: Exit the M25 at Junction 30 and take the A13 towards Southend. At the Grays exit, follow signs to the town centre. Upon reaching the one-way system, keep to the left and continue uphill for about ½ miles before turning right into Bridge Road. The ground is then on the right.

HALIFAX TOWN FC

Founded: 1911
Nickname: 'Shaymen'
Ground: Shay Ground, Shay Syke, Halifax HX1 2YS
Ground Capacity: 14,500
Seating Capacity: 7,500
Record Attendance: 36,885 (14/2/53)
Pitch Size: 110 × 75 yards

Colours: Blue and White shirts with Blue shorts
Telephone Nº: (01422) 341222
Ticket Office: (01422) 341222
Fax Number: (01422) 349487
Web Site: www.halifaxafc.co.uk
E-mail: theshay@halifaxafc.co.uk

GENERAL INFORMATION
Car Parking: Shaw Hill Car Park (Nearby)
Coach Parking: Shaw Hill
Nearest Railway Station: Halifax (5 minutes walk)
Nearest Bus Station: Halifax (10 minutes walk)
Club Shop: At the ground
Opening Times: Please phone for details
Telephone Nº: (0870) 411-7111

GROUND INFORMATION
Away Supporters' Entrances & Sections:
North Stand

ADMISSION INFO (2005/2006 PRICES)
Adult Standing: £12.00
Adult Seating: £12.00
Under-16s/Senior Citizen Standing: £6.00
Under-16s/Senior Citizen Seating: £6.00
Under-12s Standing/Seating: £3.00
Programme Price: £2.50

DISABLED INFORMATION
Wheelchairs: 10 spaces available in the disabled section,
12 spaces available on the new North Terrace
Facilities for the visually impaired may be available.
Helpers: One admitted free with each paying disabled fan
Prices: Normal prices apply for the disabled. Free for helpers
Disabled Toilets: In the Main Stand and the new North and South Terraces
Contact: (01422) 434212 (Bookings are not necessary)

Travelling Supporters' Information:
Routes: From the North: Take the A629 to Halifax Town Centre. Take the 2nd exit at the roundabout into Broad Street and follow signs for Huddersfield (A629) into Skircoat Road; From the South, East and West: Exit the M62 at Junction 24 and follow Halifax (A629) signs for the Town Centre into Skircoat Road then Shaw Hill for ground.

HEREFORD UNITED FC

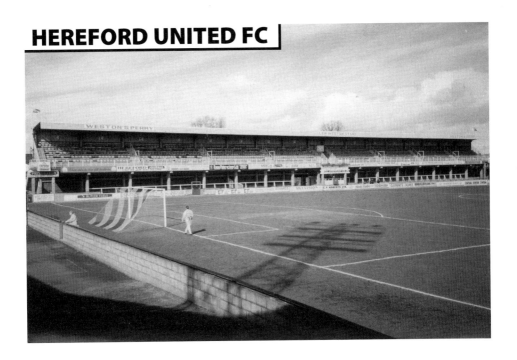

Founded: 1924	**Colours**: White shirts with White shorts
Former Names: None	**Telephone Nº**: (01432) 276666
Nickname: 'United' 'The Bulls'	**Fax Number**: (01432) 341359
Ground: Edgar Street, Hereford HR4 9JU	**Ground Capacity**: 7,873
Record Attendance: 18,114 (4/1/58)	**Seating Capacity**: 2,761
Pitch Size: 112 × 78 yards	**Web site**: www.herefordunited.co.uk

GENERAL INFORMATION
Supporters Club: None
Car Parking: Merton Meadow Car Park
Coach Parking: Cattle Market (Near the ground)
Nearest Railway Station: Hereford (½ mile)
Nearest Bus Station: Commercial Road, Hereford
Club Shop: At the ground
Opening Times: Weekdays 9.00am to 4.00pm and Matchdays 12.00pm to 3.00pm
Telephone Nº: (01432) 276666
Police Telephone Nº: (01432) 276422

GROUND INFORMATION
Away Supporters' Entrances & Sections:
Blackfriars Street and Edgar Street for the Blackfriars Street End

ADMISSION INFO (2005/2006 PRICES)
Adult Standing: £10.00
Adult Seating: £12.00
Child Standing: £6.00
Child Seating: £9.00
Senior Citizen Standing: £6.00   (Members only)
Senior Citizen Seating: £9.00   (Members only)
Note: Prices are higher if the club is in a top 5 League position
Programme Price: £2.00

DISABLED INFORMATION
Wheelchairs: 10 spaces in total for Home and Away fans in the disabled section, Merton Meadow Stand
Helpers: One helper admitted per disabled person
Prices: £6.00 for the disabled. Helpers are charged £7.00
Disabled Toilets: Yes
Contact: (01432) 276666   (Bookings are not necessary)

Travelling Supporters' Information:
Routes: From the North: Follow A49 Hereford signs straight into Edgar Street; From the East: Take the A465 or A438 into Hereford Town Centre, then follow signs for Leominster (A49) into Edgar Street; From the South: Take the A49 or A45 into the Town Centre (then as East); From the West: Take the A438 into the Town Centre (then as East).

KIDDERMINSTER HARRIERS FC

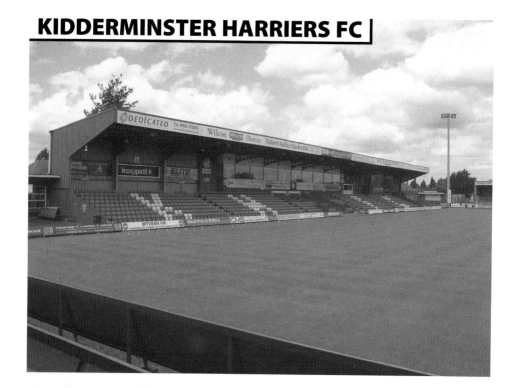

Founded: 1886
Nickname: 'Harriers'
Ground: Aggborough, Hoo Road, Kidderminster, Worcestershire DY10 1NB
Ground Capacity: 6,444
Seating Capacity: 3,143
Record Attendance: 9,155 (1948)

Pitch Size: 110 × 72 yards
Colours: Red shirts with White shorts
Telephone Nº: (01562) 823931
Fax Number: (01562) 827329
Web Site: www.harriers.co.uk

GENERAL INFORMATION

Car Parking: At the ground
Coach Parking: As directed
Nearest Railway Station: Kidderminster
Nearest Bus Station: Kidderminster Town Centre
Club Shop: At the ground
Opening Times: Weekdays and First Team Matchdays 9.00am to 5.00pm
Telephone Nº: (01562) 823931
Police Telephone Nº: –

GROUND INFORMATION

Away Supporters' Entrances & Sections:
John Smiths Stand Entrance D and South Terrace Entrance E

ADMISSION INFO (2005/2006 PRICES)

Adult Standing: £13.00
Adult Seating: £16.00
Concessionary Standing: £8.00
Concessionary Seating: £11.00
Programme Price: £2.50

DISABLED INFORMATION

Wheelchairs: Accommodated at the front of the John Smiths Stand
Helpers: Admitted
Prices: £10.00 for each disabled fan plus one helper
Disabled Toilets: Available by the disabled area
Contact: (01562) 823931 (Bookings are not necessary)

Travelling Supporters' Information:
Routes: Exit the M5 at Junction 3 and follow the A456 to Kidderminster. The ground is situated close by the Severn Valley Railway Station so follow the brown Steam Train signs and turn into Hoo Road about 200 yards downhill of the station. Follow the road along for ¼ mile and the ground is on the left.

MORECAMBE FC

Founded: 1920
Former Names: Woodhill Lane FC
Nickname: 'Shrimps'
Ground: Christie Park, Lancaster Road, Morecambe, LA4 5TJ
Record Attendance: 9,324 (1962)
Pitch Size: 118 × 76 yards

Colours: Red shirts with White shorts
Telephone N°: (01524) 411797
Daytime Phone N°: (01524) 411797
Fax Number: (01524) 832230
Ground Capacity: 6,300
Seating Capacity: 1,200
Web site: www.morecambefc.com

GENERAL INFORMATION
Supporters Club: c/o Club
Telephone N°: –
Car Parking: At the ground
Coach Parking: At the ground
Nearest Railway Station: Morecambe Central (½ mile)
Nearest Bus Station: Morecambe
Club Shop: At the ground
Opening Times: Weekdays & Matchdays 9.00am to 5.00pm
Telephone N°: (01524) 411797
Police Telephone N°: (01524) 411534

GROUND INFORMATION
Away Supporters' Entrances & Sections:
Entrances at the corner of the South Terrace and Lancaster Road for South Terrace accommodation (when segregated)

ADMISSION INFO (2005/2006 PRICES)
Adult Standing: £11.00
Adult Seating: £12.00
Child Standing: £4.00
Child Seating: £5.00
Senior Citizen Standing: £8.00
Senior Citizen Seating: £9.00
Programme Price: £2.00

DISABLED INFORMATION
Wheelchairs: 18 spaces available in the Disabled Stand and 20 spaces are available in the North Stand
Helpers: Admitted
Prices: Concessionary prices are charged
Disabled Toilets: Available in the North Stand
Contact: (01524) 411797 (Bookings are preferred)

Travelling Supporters' Information:
Routes: Exit the M6 at Junction 34. Then take the A683 west in Lancaster and pick up the A589 to Morecambe. At the 2nd roundabout on the outskirts of Morecambe, take the 2nd exit into Lancaster Road and the ground is on the left, approximately 800 yards.

SCARBOROUGH FC

Founded: 1879
Former Names: None
Nickname: 'Boro' 'Seadogs'
Ground: McCain Stadium, Seamer Road, Scarborough, North Yorkshire YO12 4HF
Record Attendance: 11,124 (1938)
Pitch Size: 112 × 74 yards

Colours: Red shirts with White shorts
Telephone N°: (01723) 375094
Fax Number: (01723) 366211
Ground Capacity: 6,899
Seating Capacity: 3,500
Web site: www.scarboroughfc.co.uk

GENERAL INFORMATION

Supporters Club: Stuart Canvin. 97 Seamer Road, Scarborough
Telephone N°: (07736) 228315
Car Parking: Street parking
Coach Parking: Weaponess Coach Park or near the ground
Nearest Railway Station: Scarborough Central (2 miles)
Nearest Bus Station: Town Centre (2 miles)
Club Shop: At the ground
Opening Times: Weekdays & Matchdays 9.30am – 5.00pm
Telephone N°: (01723) 375094
Police Telephone N°: (01723) 500300

GROUND INFORMATION

Away Supporters' Entrances & Sections:
West Stand turnstiles for West Stand seating only

ADMISSION INFO (2005/2006 PRICES)

Adult Admission: £10.00
Child Admission (Under 16s): £2.00
Senior Citizen Admission: £5.00
Note: Prices include seating at both ends of the ground. An extra £2.00 fee is charged for admission to the Grandstand
Programme Price: £2.50

DISABLED INFORMATION

Wheelchairs: 20 spaces in total in the Main Stand, West Stand and East Stand
Helpers: One helper admitted per wheelchair
Prices: Full-price for helpers. Free of charge for the disabled
Disabled Toilets: Available at rear of disabled area
Contact: (01723) 375094   (Bookings are necessary)

Travelling Supporters' Information:
Routes: The ground is situated on the main York to Scarborough Road (A64), ½ mile on the left past the B&Q DIY store.

SOUTHPORT FC

Founded: 1881
Former Names: Southport Vulcan FC, Southport Central FC
Nickname: 'The Sandgrounders'
Ground: Haig Avenue, Southport, Merseyside, PR8 6JZ
Record Attendance: 20,010 (1932)
Pitch Size: 115 × 78 yards

Colours: Yellow and Black shirts with Yellow shorts
Telephone N°: (01704) 533422
Fax Number: (01704) 533455
Ground Capacity: 6,001
Seating Capacity: 1,640
Web site: www.southportfc.net

GENERAL INFORMATION

Supporters Club: Grandstand Club
Telephone N°: (01704) 530182
Car Parking: Street parking
Coach Parking: Adjacent to the ground
Nearest Railway Station: Southport (1½ miles)
Nearest Bus Station: Southport Town Centre
Club Shop: At the ground
Opening Times: Matchdays from 1.30pm (or 6.30pm for evening matches).
Telephone N°: (01704) 533422
Police Telephone N°: (0151) 709-6010

GROUND INFORMATION

Away Supporters' Entrances & Sections:
Blowick End entrances

ADMISSION INFO (2005/2006 PRICES)

Adult Standing: £10.00
Adult Seating: £11.50
Child/Senior Citizen Standing: £6.50
Child/Senior Citizen Seating: £7.50
Programme Price: £2.50

DISABLED INFORMATION

Wheelchairs: Accommodated in front of the Grandstand
Helpers: Admitted
Prices: Concessionary prices charged for the disabled. Helpers are admitted free of charge
Disabled Toilets: Available at the Blowick End of the Grandstand
Contact: (01704) 533422 (Bookings are not necessary)

Travelling Supporters' Information:
Routes: Exit the M58 at Junction 3 and take the A570 to Southport. At the major roundabout (McDonalds/Tesco) go straight on into Scarisbrick New Road, pass over the brook and turn right into Haig Avenue at the mini-roundabout. The ground is on the right-hand side.

STEVENAGE BOROUGH FC

Founded: 1976
Former Names: None
Nickname: 'Boro'
Ground: Stevenage Stadium, Broadhall Way, Stevenage, Hertfordshire   SG2 8RH
Record Attendance: 8,040 (25/1/98)
Pitch Size: 110 × 70 yards

Colours: Red, Black and White shirts with Black shorts
Telephone Nº: (01438) 223223
Daytime Phone Nº: (01438) 223223
Fax Number: (01438) 743666
Ground Capacity: 8,414
Seating Capacity: 3,404
Web site: www.stevenageborofc.com

GENERAL INFORMATION

Supporters Club: Mervyn Stoke Geddis, 21 Woodland Way, Stevenage
Telephone Nº: (01438) 313236
Car Parking: Fairlands Show Ground (opposite)
Coach Parking: At the ground
Nearest Railway Station: Stevenage (1 mile)
Nearest Bus Station: Stevenage
Club Shop: At the ground
Opening Times: Monday to Saturday 10.00am to 5.00pm
Telephone Nº: (01438) 218063
Police Telephone Nº: (01438) 757000

GROUND INFORMATION

Away Supporters' Entrances & Sections:
South Terrace entrances and accommodation

ADMISSION INFO (2005/2006 PRICES)

Adult Standing: £10.00
Adult Seating: £13.00
Senior Citizen/Child Standing: £6.00 – £8.00
Senior Citizen/Child Seating: £8.00 – £10.00
Programme Price: £1.50

DISABLED INFORMATION

Wheelchairs: 10 spaces available in total by the North Terrace
Helpers: Admitted
Prices: £6.00 for the disabled. Helpers pay normal prices
Disabled Toilets: Yes
Contact: (01438) 223223   (Bookings are necessary)

Travelling Supporters' Information:
Routes: Exit the A1(M) at Junction 7 and take the B197. The ground is on the right at the 2nd roundabout.
Bus Routes: SB4 and SB5

TAMWORTH FC

Founded: 1933
Former Names: None
Nickname: 'The Lambs'
Ground: The Lamb Ground, Kettlebrook, Tamworth, B77 1AA
Record Attendance: 4,920 (3/4/48)
Pitch Size: 110 × 73 yards

Colours: Red shirts and shorts
Telephone Nº: (01827) 65798
Daytime Phone Nº: (01827) 65798
Fax Number: (01827) 62236
Ground Capacity: 4,118
Seating Capacity: 520
Web site: www.thelambs.co.uk

GENERAL INFORMATION

Supporters Club: Dave Clayton, c/o Club
Telephone Nº: (0781) 5046899
Car Parking: 200 spaces available at the ground
Coach Parking: At the ground
Nearest Railway Station: Tamworth (½ mile)
Nearest Bus Station: Tamworth (½ mile)
Club Shop: At the ground
Opening Times: Weekdays and Matchdays from 10.00am to 4.00pm
Telephone Nº: (01827) 65798
Police Telephone Nº: (01827) 61001

GROUND INFORMATION

Away Supporters' Entrances & Sections:
Gates 1 and 2 for Away supporters

ADMISSION INFO (2005/2006 PRICES)

Adult Standing: £10.00
Adult Seating: £12.00
Child/Senior Citizen Standing: £5.00
Child/Senior Citizen Seating: £8.00
Programme Price: £2.00

DISABLED INFORMATION

Wheelchairs: Accommodated
Helpers: Admitted
Prices: Normal prices apply for Wheelchair disabled. Helpers are charged concessionary rates
Disabled Toilets: Yes
Contact: (01827) 65798 (Bookings are advisable)

Travelling Supporters' Information:
Routes: Exit the M42 at Junction 10 and take the A5/A51 to the town centre following signs for Town Centre/Snowdome. The follow signs for Kettlebrook and the ground is in Kettlebrook Road, 50 yards from the traffic island by the Railway Viaduct and the Snowdome. The ground is signposted from all major roads.

WOKING FC

Founded: 1889
Former Names: None
Nickname: 'Cardinals'
Ground: Kingfield Stadium, Kingfield, Woking, Surrey   GU22 9AA
Record Attendance: 6,000 (1997)
Pitch Size: 109 × 76 yards

Colours: Shirts are Red & White halves, White shorts
Telephone N°: (01483) 772470
Daytime Phone N°: (01483) 772470
Fax Number: (01483) 888423
Ground Capacity: 6,036
Seating Capacity: 2,511
Web site: www.wokingfc.co.uk

GENERAL INFORMATION

Supporters Club: Mr. G. Burnett (Secretary), c/o Club
Telephone N°: (01483) 772470
Car Parking: Limited parking at the ground
Coach Parking: At or opposite the ground
Nearest Railway Station: Woking (1 mile)
Nearest Bus Station: Woking
Club Shop: At the ground
Opening Times: Weekdays and Matchdays
Telephone N°: (01483) 772470
Police Telephone N°: (01483) 761991

GROUND INFORMATION

Away Supporters' Entrances & Sections:
Kingfield Road when segregation is in force

ADMISSION INFO (2005/2006 PRICES)

Adult Standing: £12.00
Adult Seating: £15.00
Child Standing: £5.00
Child Seating: £6.00
Senior Citizen Standing: £10.00
Senior Citizen Seating: £11.00
Programme Price: £2.50

DISABLED INFORMATION

Wheelchairs: 8 spaces in the Leslie Gosden Stand and 8 spaces in front of the Family Stand
Helpers: Admitted
Prices: One wheelchair and helper for £11.00
Disabled Toilets: Yes – in the Leslie Gosden Stand and Family Stand area
Contact: (01483) 772470   (Bookings are necessary)

Travelling Supporters' Information:
Routes: Exit the M25 at Junction 10 and follow the A3 towards Guildford. Leave at the next junction onto the B2215 through Ripley and join the A247 to Woking. Alternatively, exit the M25 at Junction 11 and follow the A320 to Woking Town Centre. The ground is on the outskirts of Woking – follow signs on the A320 and A247.

YORK CITY FC

Founded: 1922
Nickname: 'Minstermen'
Ground: Kit Kat Crescent, York   YO30 7AQ
Ground Capacity: 9,496
Seating Capacity: 3,509
Record Attendance: 28,123 (5/3/38)
Pitch Size: 115 × 74 yards

Colours: Red shirts with White shorts
Telephone N°: (0870) 7771922
Ticket Office: (0870) 7771922 Extension 1
Fax Number: (0870) 7741993
Web Site: www.ycfc.net

GENERAL INFORMATION

Car Parking: Street parking
Coach Parking: By Police direction
Nearest Railway Station: York (1 mile)
Nearest Bus Station: York
Club Shop: At the ground
Opening Times: Weekdays 10.30am – 2.30pm and Saturday Matchdays 1.00pm–3.00pm and 4.40pm–5.30pm
Telephone N°: (0870) 7771922 Extension 4
Police Telephone N°: (01904) 631321

GROUND INFORMATION

Away Supporters' Entrances & Sections:
Grosvenor Road turnstiles for Grosvenor Road End

ADMISSION INFO (2005/2006 PRICES)

Adult Standing: £13.00
Adult Seating: £14.00 – £16.00
Child Standing: £8.00
Child Seating: £5.00 – £10.00
Note: Concessions are available in the Family Stand
Programme Price: £2.50

DISABLED INFORMATION

Wheelchairs: 18 spaces in total for Home and Away fans in the disabled section, in front of the Social Club
Helpers: One helper admitted per disabled person
Prices: £14.00 for the disabled. Free of charge for helpers
Disabled Toilets: Available at entrance to the disabled area
Commentaries are available for the blind
Contact: (0870) 7771922 (Ext. 1) (Bookings not necessary)

Travelling Supporters' Information:
Routes: From the North: Take the A1 then the A59 following signs for York. Cross the railway bridge and turn left after 2 miles into Water End. Turn right at the end following City Centre signs for nearly ½ mile then turn left into Bootham Crescent; From the South: Take the A64 and turn left after Buckles Inn onto the Outer Ring Road. Turn right onto the A19, follow City Centre signs for 1½ miles then turn left into Bootham Crescent; From the East: Take the Outer Ring Road turning left onto the A19. Then as from the South; From the West: Take the Outer Ring Road turning right onto the A19. Then as from the South.

THE NATIONWIDE FOOTBALL CONFERENCE NORTH CLUBS

Address

Riverside House, 14B High Street, Crayford, Kent   DA1 4HG

Phone (01322) 411021   **Fax** (01322) 411022

Clubs for the 2005/2006 Season

Alfreton Town FC .... Page 29
Barrow FC .... Page 30
Droylsden FC .... Page 31
Gainsborough Trinity FC .... Page 32
Harrogate Town FC .... Page 33
Hednesford Town FC .... Page 34
Hinckley United FC .... Page 35
Hucknall Town FC .... Page 36
Hyde United FC .... Page 37
Kettering Town FC.. Page 38
Lancaster City FC .... Page 39
Leigh R.M.I. FC .... Page 40
Moor Green FC... Page 41
Northwich Victoria FC .... Page 42
Nuneaton Borough FC .... Page 43
Redditch United FC .... Page 44
Stafford Rangers FC .... Page 45
Stalybridge Celtic FC .... Page 46
Vauxhall Motors FC.. Page 47
Worcester City FC... Page 48
Workington FC .... Page 49
Worksop Town FC .... Page 50

ALFRETON TOWN FC

Founded: 1959
Former Names: None
Nickname: 'Reds'
Ground: The Impact Arena, North Street, Alfreton, Derbyshire
Record Attendance: 5,023 vs Matlock Town (1960)
Pitch Size: 110 × 75 yards

Colours: Red shirts and shorts
Telephone Nº: (01773) 830277
Fax Number: (01773) 836164
Ground Capacity: 5,000
Seating Capacity: 272
Web site: www.alfretontownfc.com

GENERAL INFORMATION

Supporters Club: Ian McCroy, c/o Social Club
Telephone Nº: (01773) 830277
Car Parking: At the ground
Coach Parking: At the ground
Nearest Railway Station: Alfreton (½ mile)
Nearest Bus Station: Alfreton (5 minutes walk)
Club Shop: At the ground
Opening Times: Matchdays (including Youth & Reserves)
Telephone Nº: (01773) 830277
Police Telephone Nº: (01773) 570100

GROUND INFORMATION

Away Supporters' Entrances & Sections:
No usual segregation

ADMISSION INFO (2005/2006 PRICES)

Adult Standing: £8.00
Adult Seating: £8.00
Senior Citizen/Junior Standing: £4.00
Senior Citizen/Junior Seating: £4.00
Programme Price: £2.00

DISABLED INFORMATION

Wheelchairs: Accommodated at the front of the Stand
Helpers: Admitted
Prices: Please phone the club for information
Disabled Toilets: Available in the Executive Bar
Contact: (01773) 830277   (Bookings are not necessary)

Travelling Supporters' Information:
Routes: Exit the M1 at Junction 28 and take the A38 signposted for Derby. After 2 miles take the sliproad onto the B600 then go right at the main road towards the town centre. After ½ mile turn left down North Street and the ground is on the right after 200 yards.

BARROW FC

Founded: 1901
Former Names: None
Nickname: 'Bluebirds'
Ground: Holker Street Stadium, Barrow-in-Furness, Cumbria   LA14 5UQ
Record Attendance: 16,874 (1954)
Pitch Size: 110 × 75 yards

Colours: Blue and White shirts with Blue shorts
Matchday Telephone Nº: (01229) 820346
Weekday Telephone Nº: (01229) 823061
Fax Number: (01229) 820346/823061
Ground Capacity: 5,000
Seating Capacity: 1,064
Web site: www.barrowfc.com

GENERAL INFORMATION

Supporters Club: Bill Ablitt, c/o Club
Telephone Nº: (01229) 471617
Car Parking: Street Parking, Popular Side Car Park and Soccer Bar Car Park
Coach Parking: Adjacent to the ground
Nearest Railway Station: Barrow Central (½ mile)
Nearest Bus Station: ½ mile
Club Shop: 60 Buccleuch Street, Barrow-in-Furness, LA14 1QG
Opening Times: Monday to Wednesday & Fridays 10.00am – 4.00pm, Saturdays 10.00am – 2.00pm
Telephone Nº: (01229) 823061 (weekdays)
Police Telephone Nº: (01229) 824532

GROUND INFORMATION

Away Supporters' Entrances & Sections:
West Terrace (not covered)

ADMISSION INFO (2005/2006 PRICES)

Adult Standing: £8.00
Adult Seating: £9.00
Child Standing: £5.00
Child Seating: £6.00
Programme Price: £1.50

DISABLED INFORMATION

Wheelchairs: 6 spaces available in the Disabled Area
Helpers: Admitted
Prices: Normal prices apply
Disabled Toilets: Available
Contact: (01229) 820346   (Bookings are not necessary)

Travelling Supporters' Information:
Routes: Exit the M6 at Junction 36 and take the A590 through Ulverston. Using the bypass, follow signs for Barrow. After approximately 5 miles, turn left into Wilkie Road and the ground is on the left.

DROYLSDEN FC |

Founded: 1892
Former Names: None
Nickname: 'The Bloods'
Ground: Butchers Arms, Market Street, Droylsden, Manchester M43 7AY
Record Attendance: 5,400 (1973)
Pitch Size: 110 × 70 yards

Colours: Red shirts with Black shorts
Telephone Nº: (0161) 370-1426
Daytime Phone Nº: (0161) 370-1426
Fax Number: (0161) 370-8341
Ground Capacity: 3,500
Seating Capacity: 500
Web site: www.droylsdenfc.co.uk

GENERAL INFORMATION

Supporters Club: c/o Club
Telephone Nº: –
Car Parking: Street parking only
Coach Parking: At the ground
Nearest Railway Station: Manchester Piccadilly
Nearest Bus Station: Ashton
Club Shop: At the ground
Opening Times: Matchdays only
Telephone Nº: (0161) 370-1426
Police Telephone Nº: (0161) 330-8321

GROUND INFORMATION

Away Supporters' Entrances & Sections:
No usual segregation

ADMISSION INFO (2005/2006 PRICES)

Adult Standing: £8.00
Adult Seating: £9.00
Concessionary Standing: £5.00
Concessionary Seating: £6.00
Programme Price: £1.00

DISABLED INFORMATION

Wheelchairs: Accommodated beside the Stand
Helpers: Yes
Prices: Normal prices apply for the disabled and helpers
Disabled Toilets: Available
Contact: (0161) 370-1426   (Bookings are not necessary)

Travelling Supporters' Information:
Routes: Take the Manchester Outer Ring Road M60 and exit at Junction 23. Join the A635 towards Manchester and after the retail park on the left, take the centre lane, then turn right at the traffic lights onto the A662 signposted for Droylsden. At the next traffic lights, turn right onto Market Street and after 150 yards go straight on at the traffic lights. The entrance to the ground is 75 yards on the left.

GAINSBOROUGH TRINITY FC

Founded: 1873
Former Names: None
Nickname: 'The Blues'
Ground: Northolme, Gainsborough, Lincolnshire, DN21 2QW
Record Attendance: 9,760 (1948)
Pitch Size: 111 × 71 yards

Colours: Blue shirts with White shorts
Telephone Nº: (01427) 613295 or 615239
Clubhouse Phone Nº: (01427) 613688
Fax Number: (01427) 613295 or (01427) 615239
Ground Capacity: 4,340
Seating Capacity: 504
Web site: www.gainsboroughtrinity.com

GENERAL INFORMATION

Supporters Club: G. Burton, c/o Club
Telephone Nº: (01427) 613688
Car Parking: Street parking, in a Local Car Tyre Company car park and also in a Local Authority Car Park nearby
Coach Parking: Opposite the ground
Nearest Railway Station: Lea Road (2 miles)
Nearest Bus Station: Heaton Street (1 mile)
Club Shop: At the ground
Opening Times: Matchdays only
Telephone Nº: (01427) 611612
Police Telephone Nº: (01427) 810910

GROUND INFORMATION

Away Supporters' Entrances & Sections:
No usual segregation

ADMISSION INFO (2005/2006 PRICES)

Adult Standing: £8.00
Adult Seating: £9.00
Concessionary Standing: £6.00
Concessionary Seating: £7.00
Under 16s are admitted for £1.00 when with a paying adult
Programme Price: £1.50

DISABLED INFORMATION

Wheelchairs: Accommodated
Helpers: Please phone the club for information
Prices: Normal prices for the disabled. Free for helpers
Disabled Toilets: Available adjacent to the Main Stand
Contact: (01427) 613295 (Bookings are not necessary)

Travelling Supporters' Information:
Routes: From the North, South and West: Exit the A1 at Blyth services taking the 1st left through to Bawtry. In Bawtry, turn right at the traffic lights onto the A631 straight through to Gainsborough (approx. 11 miles). Go over the bridge to the second set of traffic lights and turn left onto the A159 (Scunthorpe Road). Follow the main road past Tesco on the right through the traffic lights. The ground is 250 yards on right; From the East: Take the A631 into Gainsborough and turn right onto the A159. Then as above.

HARROGATE TOWN FC

Founded: 1919
Former Names: Harrogate FC and Harrogate Hotspurs FC
Nickname: 'Town'
Ground: Wetherby Road, Harrogate   HG2 7SA
Record Attendance: 4,280 (1950)
Pitch Size: 107 × 72 yards

Colours: Yellow and Black striped shirts, Black shorts
Telephone Nº: (01423) 880675 or 883671
Contact Nº: (01423) 525341 (Club Secretary)
Contact Fax Number: (01423) 525341
Club Fax Number: (01423) 880675
Ground Capacity: 3,290
Seating Capacity: 502
Web site: www.harrogatetown.com

GENERAL INFORMATION

Supporters Club: c/o Phil Harrison, 10 Fieldway Close, Harrogate
Telephone/Fax Nº: (01423) 525211
Car Parking: Hospital Car Park adjacent
Coach Parking: At the ground
Nearest Railway Station: Harrogate (¾ mile)
Nearest Bus Station: Harrogate
Club Shop: At the ground
Opening Times: Matchdays only
Telephone Nº: (01423) 325111
Police Telephone Nº: (01423) 505541

GROUND INFORMATION

Away Supporters' Entrances & Sections:
No usual segregation

ADMISSION INFO (2005/2006 PRICES)

Adult Standing: £10.00
Adult Seating: £11.00
Concessionary Standing: £5.00
Concessionary Seating: £6.00
Under-12s Standing: £2.00
Under-12s Seating: £3.00
Programme Price: £2.00

DISABLED INFORMATION

Wheelchairs: Accommodated at the front of the Main Stand
Helpers: Admitted
Prices: Free for the disabled when accompanied by a helper. Normal prices for helpers
Disabled Toilets: Available
Contact: (01423) 880675 (Bookings are not necessary)

Travelling Supporters' Information:
Routes: From the South: Take the A61 from Leeds and turn right at the roundabout onto the ring road (signposted York). After about 1¼ miles turn left at the next roundabout onto A661 Wetherby Road. The ground is situated ¾ mile on the right; From the West: Take the A59 straight into Wetherby Road from Empress Roundabout and the ground is on the left; From the East & North: Exit the A1(M) at Junction 47, take the A59 to Harrogate then follow the Southern bypass to Wetherby Road for the A661 Roundabout. Turn right towards Harrogate Town Centre and the ground is on the right after ¾ mile.

HEDNESFORD TOWN FC

Founded: 1880
Former Names: Formed by the amalgamation of West Hill FC and Hill Top FC
Nickname: 'The Pitmen'
Ground: Keys Park, Keys Park Road, Hednesford, Cannock   WS12 2DZ
Record Attendance: 3,169 (13th January 1997)
Pitch Size: 109 × 72 yards

Colours: White shirts with Black shorts
Telephone N°: (01543) 422870
Daytime Phone N°: (01543) 422870
Fax Number: (01543) 428180
Ground Capacity: 6,039
Seating Capacity: 1,010
Web site: www.hednesfordtown.com

GENERAL INFORMATION

Supporters Club: Paul Acton, c/o Club
Telephone N°: (07785) 710267
Car Parking: 500 spaces available at the ground – £1.00 fee
Coach Parking: At the ground
Nearest Railway Station: Hednesford (1 mile)
Nearest Bus Station: Hednesford
Club Shop: At the ground
Opening Times: Matchdays and Weekdays 9.00am–5.00pm
Telephone N°: (01543) 422870
Police Telephone N°: (01543) 574545

GROUND INFORMATION

Away Supporters' Entrances & Sections:
Hednesford End when segregation is required

ADMISSION INFO (2005/2006 PRICES)

Adult Standing: £8.00
Adult Seating: £9.50
Child Standing: £4.50 (Under 16s season ticket £20.00)
Child Seating: £5.50
Programme Price: £1.80

DISABLED INFORMATION

Wheelchairs: 8 spaces available in front of the Main Stand
Helpers: Please contact the club for details
Prices: Please contact the club for details
Disabled Toilets: 2 are available – one in the Main Building, one in the Hednesford End of the stand
Contact: (01543) 422870 (Bookings are necessary)

Travelling Supporters' Information:
Routes: Exit the M6 at Junction 11 or the M6 Toll T7 and follow signs for A460 (Rugeley). After cross the A5 at Churchbridge Island, continue on the A460. After five traffic islands pick up signs for Hednesford Town FC/Keys Park and follow to the ground.

HINCKLEY UNITED FC

Founded: 1889
Former Names: Formed when Hinckley Athletic FC merged with Hinckley Town FC in 1997 (previously Westfield Rovers FC)
Nickname: 'The Knitters'
Ground: Marstons Stadium, Leicester Road, Hinckley, LE10 3DR
Record Attendance: 2,029 (2005)

Pitch Size: 110 × 72 yards
Colours: Shirts are Blue with a Red side panel, shorts are Blue
Telephone Nº: (01455) 840088
Contact Number: (01455) 447278
Ground Capacity: 4,329
Seating Capacity: 630
Web site: www.hinckleyunitedfc.co.uk

GENERAL INFORMATION

Supporters Club: c/o Club
Telephone Nº: (01455) 840088
Car Parking: At the ground
Coach Parking: At the ground
Nearest Railway Station: Hinckley (2 miles)
Nearest Bus Station: Hinckley
Club Shop: At the ground
Opening Times: Matchdays only
Telephone Nº: (01455) 840088
Police Telephone Nº: (0116) 222-2222

GROUND INFORMATION

Away Supporters' Entrances & Sections:
West Stand and Terrace if required (no usual segregation)

ADMISSION INFO (2005/2006 PRICES)

Adult Standing: £8.00
Adult Seating: £9.00
Under-16s Standing: £3.00
Under-16s Seating: £4.00
Senior Citizen Standing: £5.00
Senior Citizen Seating: £6.00
Programme Price: £2.00

DISABLED INFORMATION

Wheelchairs: Accommodated
Helpers: Admitted
Prices: Normal prices apply
Disabled Toilets: Yes
Contact: (01455) 840088   (Bookings are not necessary)

Travelling Supporters' Information:
Routes: From the North-West: Take the A5 southbound and take the 1st exit at Dodwells roundabout onto the A47 towards Earl Shilton. Go straight on over 3 roundabouts then take the 3rd exit at the next roundabout onto the B4668. The entrance to the ground is on the right after 200 yards; From the South: Take the A5 northbound and upon reaching Dodwells roundabout take the 2nd exit onto the A47 towards East Shilton. Then as above; From the North-East: Take the M69, exit at Junction 2 and follow the B4669 towards Hinckley. After 2 miles (passing through 2 sets of traffic lights) bear right into Spa Lane then turn right at the next set of traffic lights onto the B4668 towards Earl Shilton. The Stadium is on the left after 1¾ miles.

HUCKNALL TOWN FC

Founded: 1946
Former Names: Hucknall Colliery Welfare FC
Nickname: 'The Town'
Ground: Watnall Road, Hucknall, Nottinghamshire, NG15 7LP
Record Attendance: 1,836 (9th April 2005)
Pitch Size: 111 × 72 yards

Colours: Yellow shirts with Black shorts
Telephone Nº: (0115) 956-1253
Daytime Nº: (0115) 963-0206 (matchdays)
Fax Number: (0115) 963-0716
Ground Capacity: 3,000
Seating Capacity: 500
Web site: www.hucknalltownfc.com

GENERAL INFORMATION
Supporters Club: Mike Drury
Telephone Nº: (0115) 963-0206
Car Parking: Available at the ground
Coach Parking: At the ground
Nearest Railway Station: Hucknall (1 mile)
Nearest Bus Station: Broadmarsh, Nottingham (change for Hucknall)
Club Shop: At the ground
Opening Times: Matchdays or by appointment only
Telephone Nº: (0115) 963-0206
Police Telephone Nº: (0115) 968-0999

GROUND INFORMATION
Away Supporters' Entrances & Sections:
No usual segregation

ADMISSION INFO (2005/2006 PRICES)
Adult Standing: £8.00
Adult Seating: £8.00
Child Standing: £2.00
Child Seating: £2.00
Senior Citizen Standing: £6.00
Senior Citizen Seating: £6.00
Programme Price: £1.50

DISABLED INFORMATION
Wheelchairs: Accommodated
Helpers: Admitted
Prices: Concessionary prices are charged
Disabled Toilets: One available
Contact: (0115) 963-0206 (Bookings are not necessary)

Travelling Supporters' Information:
Routes: Exit the M1 at Junction 27 and take the A608 towards Hucknall. Turn right onto the A611 to Hucknall then take the Hucknall bypass. At the second roundabout join Watnall Road (B6009) and the ground is 100 yards on the right.

HYDE UNITED FC

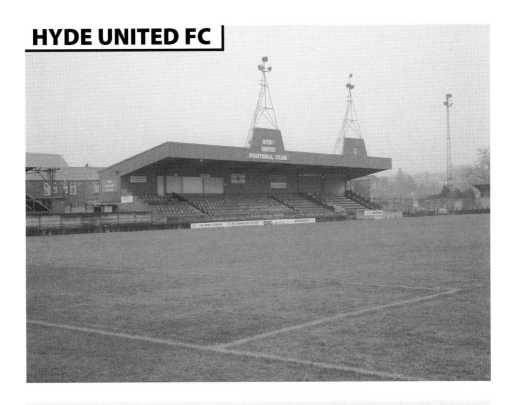

Founded: 1919
Former Names: Hyde FC (1885-1917)
Nickname: 'Tigers'
Ground: Tameside Stadium, Ewen Fields,
Walker Lane, Hyde, Cheshire SK14 2SB
Record Attendance: 9,500 (1952)
Pitch Size: 114 × 70 yards
Colours: Red shirts with White shorts

Telephone N°: (0161) 368-1031 (Matchdays)
Daytime Phone N°: (0161) 368-1031 or
(07778) 792502 (Secretary)
Fax Number: (0161) 367-7273 (Ground);
(01270) 212473 (Secretary)
Ground Capacity: 4,100
Seating Capacity: 550
Web site: www.hydeunited.co.uk

GENERAL INFORMATION
Supporters Club: Mark Dring, 16 Gainsborough Walk,
Denton, Manchester M34 6NS
Telephone N°: (0161) 336-8076
Car Parking: 150 spaces available at the ground
Coach Parking: At the ground
Nearest Railway Station: Newton (¼ mile)
Nearest Bus Station: Hyde
Club Shop: At the ground
Opening Times: Matchdays only
Telephone N°: (0161) 368-1031
Police Telephone N°: (0161) 330-8321

GROUND INFORMATION
Away Supporters' Entrances & Sections:
No usual segregation although it is used as required

ADMISSION INFO (2005/2006 PRICES)
Adult Standing: £8.00
Adult Seating: £9.00
Child Standing: £3.00
Child Seating: £4.00
Senior Citizen Standing: £3.00
Senior Citizen Seating: £4.00
Programme Price: £1.50

DISABLED INFORMATION
Wheelchairs: Accommodated in the disabled area
Helpers: Please phone the club for information
Prices: Please phone the club for information
Disabled Toilets: Yes
Contact: (01270) 212473 (Bookings are not necessary)

Travelling Supporters' Information:
Routes: On entering Hyde follow signs for Tameside Leisure Park. When on Walker Lane, take the 2nd Car Park entrance near
the Leisure Pool and follow the road round for the Stadium.

KETTERING TOWN FC

Founded: 1872
Former Names: None
Nickname: 'The Poppies'
Ground: Rockingham Road, Kettering, Northants. NN16 9AW
Record Attendance: 11,526 (1947-48)
Pitch Size: 110 × 70 yards

Colours: Red shirts and shorts
Telephone Nº: (01536) 483028/410815
Daytime Phone Nº: (01536) 483028
Fax Number: (01536) 412273
Ground Capacity: 6,264
Seating Capacity: 1,747
Web site: www.ketteringtownfc.co.uk
E-mail: info@ketteringtownfc.co.uk

GENERAL INFORMATION

Supporters Club: c/o Club
Car Parking: At the ground
Coach Parking: At the 'Beeswing' Public House
Nearest Railway Station: Kettering (1 mile)
Nearest Bus Station: Kettering (1 mile)
Club Shop: At the ground. Also at Elmore's News Shop in Silver Street, Kettering
Opening Times: Shop hours in the Town Centre shop and on request at the ground on Matchdays
Telephone Nº: (01536) 483028
Police Telephone Nº: (01536) 411411

GROUND INFORMATION

Away Supporters' Entrances & Sections:
Rockingham Road End accommodation

ADMISSION INFO (2005/2006 PRICES)

Adult Standing: £8.50
Adult Seating: £10.50
Senior Citizen Standing: £6.00
Senior Citizen Seating: £8.00
Note: Children up to the age of 16 years may apply for a £37.00 season ticket.
Programme Price: £2.00

DISABLED INFORMATION

Wheelchairs: 12 spaces are available on the terracing adjacent to the Main Stand
Helpers: One helper admitted per wheelchair
Prices: Free of charge for the disabled
Disabled Toilets: Available next to the Social Club
Contact: (01536) 483028 (Bookings are not necessary)

Travelling Supporters' Information:
Routes: To reach Kettering from the A1, M1 or M6, use the A14 to Junction 7, follow the A43 for 1 mile, turn right at the roundabout and the ground is 400 yards on the left on the A6003. (The ground is situated to the North of Kettering (1 mile) on the main A6003 Rockingham Road to Oakham).

LANCASTER CITY FC

Founded: 1905
Former Names: Lancaster Athletic FC,
Lancaster Town FC and City of Lancaster AFC
Nickname: 'Dolly Blues'
Ground: Giant Axe, West Road, Lancaster LA1 5PE
Record Attendance: 7,500 (1936)
Pitch Size: 110 × 70 yards

Colours: Sky Blue shirts and shorts
Telephone Nº: (01524) 382238/841710 (Office)
Ground Phone Nº: (01524) 382238
Fax Number: (01524) 382238
Ground Capacity: 3,153
Seating Capacity: 513
Web site: www.lancastercityfc.com

GENERAL INFORMATION

Supporters Club: At the Dolly Blue Tavern
Telephone Nº: (01524) 843500
Car Parking: At the ground
Coach Parking: At the ground
Nearest Railway Station: Lancaster (2 minutes walk)
Nearest Bus Station: Lancaster (5 minutes walk)
Club Shop: At the ground
Opening Times: Matchdays only
Telephone Nº: None
Police Telephone Nº: (01524) 63333

GROUND INFORMATION

Away Supporters' Entrances & Sections:
No usual segregation

ADMISSION INFO (2005/2006 PRICES)

Adult Standing: £8.00
Adult Seating: £8.00
Concession/Child Standing: £5.00
Concession/Child Seating: £5.00
Children under the age of 4 are admitted free of charge
Programme Price: £1.50

DISABLED INFORMATION

Wheelchairs: Accommodated
Helpers: Admitted
Prices: Normal prices apply
Disabled Toilets: Yes
Contact: (01524) 382238 (Bookings are not necessary)

Travelling Supporters' Information:
Routes: From the South: Exit the M6 at Junction 33 and follow Railway Station signs into the City. Turn left at the traffic lights after Waterstones Bookshop then take the second right passing the Railway Station on the right. Follow the road down the hill and the ground is 1st right; From the North: Exit the M6 at Junction 34 and bear left onto the A683. Go into the one-way system in the City and pass the Police Station. At the next traffic lights by the Alexandra pub, follow the road back into the centre, then as from the South, following Railway Station signs.

LEIGH RMI FC

Founded: 1896
Former Names: Horwich RMI FC
Nickname: 'The Railwaymen'
Ground: Hilton Park, Kirkhall Lane, Leigh, WN7 1RN
Record Attendance: 9,853 (1949)

Pitch Size: 112 × 75 yards
Colours: Red and White shirts with Red shorts
Telephone N°: (01772) 719266
Fax Number: (01772) 719266
Ground Capacity: 8,500
Seating Capacity: 1,425

GENERAL INFORMATION

Supporters Club: c/o Club
Car Parking: 150 spaces available at the ground
Coach Parking: At the ground
Nearest Railway Station: Atherton
Nearest Bus Station: Leigh
Club Shop: At the ground
Opening Times: Daily
Telephone N°: (01942) 743743
Police Telephone N°: (01942) 244981

GROUND INFORMATION

Away Supporters' Entrances & Sections:
No usual segregation

ADMISSION INFO (2005/2006 PRICES)

Adult Standing: £8.00
Adult Seating: £8.00
Child/Senior Citizen Standing: £4.00
Child/Senior Citizen Seating: £4.00
Junior Members Standing/Seating: £1.00
Programme Price: £1.50

DISABLED INFORMATION

Wheelchairs: Accommodated by arrangement
Helpers: Admitted
Prices: Normal prices apply
Disabled Toilets: Four available at the ground
Contact: (01772) 719266 (Bookings are not necessary)

Travelling Supporters' Information:
Routes: Exit the M61 at Junction 5 and follow the Westhoughton sign to the roundabout then follow signs for Leigh. Stay on the main road to the traffic lights, turn left into Leigh Road and carry on for about 3 miles until the traffic lights. Turn left and then 1st right at the next set of traffic lights. Turn right onto Atheleigh Way (A579) at the first set of traffic lights and turn left (B & Q on the right), at the next set of traffic lights. Turn right (Leigh Town Centre), at the second opening on the right turn into Prescott Street, carry on to the top, turn right and the ground is on the left.

MOOR GREEN FC

Founded: 1901
Former Names: None
Nickname: 'The Moors'
Ground: The Moorlands, Sherwood Road, Hall Green, Birmingham   B28 0EX
Record Attendance: 5,000 (1951)
Pitch Size: 115 × 73 yards
Correspondence: N. Collins, 7 The Morelands, West Heath, Birmingham   B31 3HA

Colours: Shirts – Sky & Dark Blue halves
Shorts – Dark Blue
Telephone Nº: (0121) 777-8961
Contact Number: (0121) 476-4944 or (07801) 248211
Ground Capacity: 3,250
Seating Capacity: 250
Web site: www.moorgreenfc.co.uk

GENERAL INFORMATION
Supporters Club: c/o Club
Telephone Nº: (0121) 777-8961
Car Parking: 200 spaces available at the ground
Coach Parking: At the ground
Nearest Railway Station: Hall Green/Yardley Wood (1 mile)
Nearest Bus Station: Digbeth
Club Shop: At the ground
Opening Times: Matchdays only (30 minutes before and after the game)
Telephone Nº: (0121) 777-8961
Police Telephone Nº: (0121) 626-7030

GROUND INFORMATION
Away Supporters' Entrances & Sections: Sherwood Road entrances

ADMISSION INFO (2005/2006 PRICES)
Adult Standing: £9.00
Adult Seating: £9.00
Senior Citizen Standing: £4.00
Senior Citizen Seating: £4.00
Child Standing: £4.00
Child Seating: £4.00
Programme Price: £1.50

DISABLED INFORMATION
Wheelchairs: Accommodated
Helpers: Admitted
Prices: Normal prices apply for the disabled and helpers
Disabled Toilets: None
Contact: (0121) 777-8961   (Bookings are not necessary)

Travelling Supporters' Information:
Routes: Exit the M42 at Junction 4 and follow signs to Shirley (approximately 3 miles). Take the A34 through Shirley into Hall Green. At Robin Hood Roundabout, take the 2nd exit into Robin Hood Lane and continue along for 1 mile. At the next roundabout turn right and Sherwood Road is approximately 600 yards on the left.

NORTHWICH VICTORIA FC

Founded: 1874
Former Names: None
Nickname: 'The Vics' 'The Greens' 'The Trickies'
Ground: Victoria Stadium, Wincham Avenue,
Wincham, Northwich CW9 6GB
Record Attendance: –
Pitch Size: 112 × 74 yards

Colours: Green & White hooped shirts, White shorts
Office Telephone Nº: (01606) 41450
Fax Number: (01606) 330577
Ground Capacity: 5,294
Seating Capacity: 1,294
Web site: www.nvfc.co.uk

GENERAL INFORMATION

Supporters Club: Peter Grimes, c/o Club
Telephone Nº: (01606) 41450
Car Parking: Ample parking spaces available at the ground
Coach Parking: At the ground
Nearest Railway Station: Northwich (2½ miles)
Nearest Bus Station: Northwich (2½ miles)
Club Shop: At the ground
Opening Times: Weekdays & Matchdays 10.00am–4.00pm
Telephone Nº: (01606) 41555
Police Telephone Nº: (01606) 48000

GROUND INFORMATION

Away Supporters' Entrances & Sections: Not specified

ADMISSION INFO (2005/2006 PRICES)

Adult Standing: £10.50
Adult Seating: £12.50
Senior Citizen Standing: £8.50
Senior Citizen Seating: £10.50
Under-16s Standing: £4.50
Under-16s Seating: £6.50
Under-12s Standing/Seating: £2.00
Programme Price: £2.00

DISABLED INFORMATION

Wheelchairs: 46 spaces are available in total
Helpers: Admitted
Prices: Free for the disabled. Helpers pay normal prices
Disabled Toilets: Yes
Contact: (01606) 41450   (Please phone to book)

Travelling Supporters' Information:
Routes: Exit the M6 at Junction 19 and take the A556 towards Northwich. After 3 miles turn right onto the A559 following signs for Warrington. Turn left after Marston opposite the Black Greyhound Inn then left into Wincham Avenue after 200 yards. Alternative Route: Exit the M56 at Junction 10 and take the A559 to the Black Greyhound Inn then turn right. Then as above

NUNEATON BOROUGH FC

The club expect to move to a new stadium in Liberty Way early in 2006.
Please contact the club directly for further information.

Founded: 1937 (Reformed 1991)
Former Names: Nuneaton Town FC
Nickname: 'Boro'
Ground: Manor Park, Beaumont Road, Nuneaton, Warwickshire   CV11 5HD
Record Attendance: 22,114 (1967)
Pitch Size: 112 × 77 yards

Colours: Blue shirts and white shorts
Telephone Nº: (024) 7638-5738
Daytime Phone Nº: (024) 7638-5738
Fax Number: (024) 7634-2690
Ground Capacity: 6,000
Seating Capacity: 600
Web site: www.nbafc.net

GENERAL INFORMATION
Supporters Club: c/o Manor Park
Car Parking: Street parking only
Coach Parking: At the ground
Nearest Railway Station: Nuneaton (2 miles)
Nearest Bus Station: Nuneaton (2 miles)
Club Shop: Yes – The Boro Shop
Opening Times: Daily from 10.00am to 4.00pm
Telephone Nº: (024) 7638-5738
Police Telephone Nº: (024) 7664-1111

GROUND INFORMATION
Away Supporters' Entrances & Sections:
Top Cock and Bear entrances for Canal Side accommodation when segregated

ADMISSION INFO (2005/2006 PRICES)
Adult Standing: £8.00
Adult Seating: £10.00
Child Standing: £3.00
Child Seating: £4.00
Concessionary Standing: £5.00
Concessionary Seating: £6.00
Programme Price: £2.00

DISABLED INFORMATION
Wheelchairs: Accommodated
Helpers: Please phone the club for information
Prices: Please phone the club for information
Disabled Toilets: Available at rear of Main Stand
Contact: (024) 7638-5738   (Bookings are not necessary)

Travelling Supporters' Information:
Routes: Exit the M6 at Junction 3 and take the A444 to Nuneaton. At the roundabout by the hospital immediately after the pedestrian overbridge, turn left into College Street to the Bull Ring. Turn right into Greenmoor Road and follow ¾ mile to the end, then turn right and cross over the bridge – the ground is on the left.

REDDITCH UNITED FC

Founded: 1891	**Colours**: Red shirts, shorts and socks
Former Names: Redditch Town FC	**Telephone Nº**: (01527) 67450
Nickname: 'The Reds'	**Contact Nº**: (01527) 876913
Ground: Valley Stadium, Bromsgrove Road, Redditch B97 4RN	**Fax Number**: (01527) 60611
Record Attendance: 5,500 (vs Bromsgrove 1954/55)	**Ground Capacity**: 5,000
Pitch Size: 110 × 72 yards	**Seating Capacity**: 400
	Web site: www.redditchunited.com

GENERAL INFORMATION

Supporters Club: c/o Club
Telephone Nº: (01527) 67450
Car Parking: At the ground
Coach Parking: At the ground
Nearest Railway Station: Redditch (¼ mile)
Nearest Bus Station: Redditch (¼ mile)
Club Shop: None

GROUND INFORMATION

Away Supporters' Entrances & Sections:
No segregation

ADMISSION INFO (2005/2006 PRICES)

Adult Standing: £9.00
Adult Seating: £10.00
Senior Citizen Standing: £6.00
Senior Citizen Seating: £6.00
Under-12s: £2.00 when accompanied by a paying adult
Programme Price: £1.60

DISABLED INFORMATION

Wheelchairs: Accommodated
Helpers: Admitted
Prices: Normal prices apply to both helpers and disabled
Disabled Toilets: Available
Contact: (01527) 67450 (Bookings are not necessary)

Travelling Supporters' Information:
Routes: Exit the M42 at Junction 2 and follow the A441 towards Redditch. Take the 4th exit at the roundabout (signposted Batchley) and turn left at the traffic lights into Birmingham Road. Take the next right into Clive Road then left into Hewell Road. Continue to the T-junction and turn right, passing the Railway Station on the right. Continue through the traffic lights and the ground is situated on the right hand side after about ¼ mile.

STAFFORD RANGERS FC

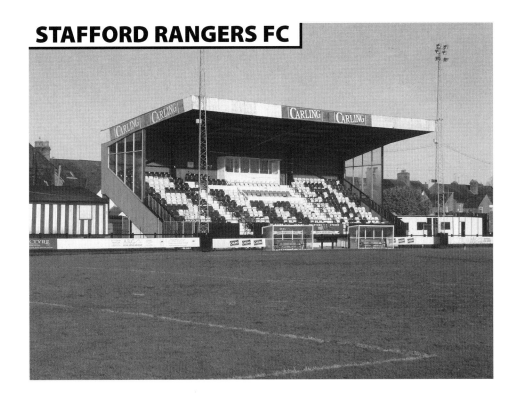

Founded: 1876
Former Names: None
Nickname: 'The Boro'
Ground: Marston Road, Stafford   ST16 3BX
Record Attendance: 8,523 (4/1/75)
Pitch Size: 112 × 75 yards

Colours: Black and White striped shirts, Black shorts
Telephone Nº: (01785) 602430
Social Club Nº: (01785) 602432
Ground Capacity: 3,472
Seating Capacity: 426
Web site: www.staffordrangers.co.uk

GENERAL INFORMATION
Supporters Club: c/o Social Club
Telephone Nº: (01785) 602432
Car Parking: At the ground
Coach Parking: Astonfields Road
Nearest Railway Station: Stafford (1½ miles)
Nearest Bus Station: Stafford
Club Shop: At the ground
Opening Times: Matchdays only
Telephone Nº: (01785) 602430
Police Telephone Nº: (01785) 258151

GROUND INFORMATION
Away Supporters' Entrances & Sections:
Lotus End

ADMISSION INFO (2005/2006 PRICES)
Adult Standing: £9.00
Adult Seating: £11.00
Concessionary Standing: £5.00
Concessionary Seating: £7.00
Children under the age of 12 are admitted for £2.00 when accompanied by a paying adult
Programme Price: £2.00

DISABLED INFORMATION
Wheelchairs: Accommodated at Marston Road End
Helpers: Admitted
Prices: Concessionary prices for the disabled. Normal prices for helpers
Disabled Toilets: None
Contact: (01785) 602430   (Bookings are not necessary)

Travelling Supporters' Information:
Routes: Exit the M6 at Junction 14 and take the slip road signposted 'Stone/Stafford'. Continue to traffic island and go straight across then take the 3rd exit on the right into Common Road, signposted 'Common Road/Aston Fields Industrial Estate'. Follow the road to the bridge and bear left over the bridge. The ground is on the right.

STALYBRIDGE CELTIC FC

Founded: 1909
Former Names: None
Nickname: 'Celtic'
Ground: Bower Fold, Mottram Road, Stalybridge, Cheshire SK15 2RT
Record Attendance: 9,753 (1922/23)
Pitch Size: 109 × 70 yards

Colours: Blue shirts and shorts
Telephone Nº: (0161) 338-2828
Daytime Phone Nº: (0161) 338-2828
Fax Number: (0161) 338-8256
Ground Capacity: 6,108
Seating Capacity: 1,155
Web site: www.stalybridgeceltic.co.uk

GENERAL INFORMATION
Supporters Club: Bob Rhodes, c/o Club
Telephone Nº: (01457) 764044
Car Parking: At the ground
Coach Parking: At the ground
Nearest Railway Station: Stalybridge (1 mile)
Nearest Bus Station: Stalybridge town centre
Club Shop: At the ground
Opening Times: Matchdays and by arrangement
Telephone Nº: (0161) 338-2828
Police Telephone Nº: (0161) 330-8321

GROUND INFORMATION
Away Supporters' Entrances & Sections:
Lockwood & Greenwood Stand

ADMISSION INFO (2005/2006 PRICES)
Adult Standing: £8.00
Adult Seating: £9.00
Child Standing: £5.00
Child Seating: £6.00
Programme Price: £1.50

DISABLED INFORMATION
Wheelchairs: 20 spaces available each for home and away fans at the side of the Stepan Stand. A further 9 spaces available in the new Lord Tom Pendry Stand
Helpers: Please phone the club for information
Prices: Please phone the club for information
Disabled Toilets: Available at the rear of the Stepan Stand and at the side of the Lord Tom Pendry Stand
Contact: (0161) 338-2828 (Bookings are necessary)

Travelling Supporters' Information:
Routes: From the Midlands and South: Take the M6, M56, M60 and M67, leaving at the end of the motorway. Go across the roundabout to the traffic lights and turn left. The ground is approximately 2 miles on the left before the Hare & Hounds pub; From the North: Exit the M62 at Junction 18 onto the M60 singposted for Ashton-under-Lyne. Follow the M60 to Junction 24 and join the M67, then as from the Midlands and South.

VAUXHALL MOTORS FC

Founded: 1963
Former Names: Vauxhall GM FC
Nickname: 'Motormen'
Ground: Rivacre Park, Hooton, Ellesmere Port, Cheshire   CH66 1NJ
Record Attendance: 1,500 (1987)
Pitch Size: 110 × 70 yards
Colours: White shirts with Dark Blue shorts

Telephone Nº: (0151) 328-1114 (Ground)
Ground Capacity: 2,500
Seating Capacity: 350
Contact: Carole Paisey, 31 South Road, West Kirby, Wirral   CH48 3HG
Contact Phone and Fax Nº: (0151) 625-6936
Web site: www.vmfc.com
E-mail: office@vmfc.com

GENERAL INFORMATION
Supporters Club: At the ground
Telephone/Fax Nº: (0151) 328-1144
Car Parking: At the ground
Coach Parking: At the ground
Nearest Railway Station: Hooton
Nearest Bus Station: Ellesmere Port
Club Shop: At the ground
Opening Times: Matchdays only
Telephone Nº: –

GROUND INFORMATION
Away Supporters' Entrances & Sections:
No usual segregation

ADMISSION INFO (2005/2006 PRICES)
Adult Standing/Seating: £8.00
Child Standing/Seating: £4.00
Senior Citizen Standing/Seating: £5.00
Programme Price: £2.00

DISABLED INFORMATION
Wheelchairs: Accommodated as necessary
Helpers: Admitted
Prices: Normal prices for the disabled. Free for helpers
Disabled Toilets: Available
Contact: –   (Bookings are not necessary)

Travelling Supporters' Information:
Routes: Exit the M53 at Junction 5 and take the A41 towards Chester. Turn left at the first set of traffic lights into Hooton Green. Turn left at the first T-junction then right at the next T-junction into Rivacre Road. The ground is situated 250 yards on the right.

WORCESTER CITY FC

Founded: 1902
Former Names: Berwick Rangers FC
Nickname: 'The City'
Ground: St. Georges Lane, Worcester   WR1 1QT
Record Attendance: 17,042 (1958/59)
Pitch Size: 110 × 75 yards

Colours: Blue and White shirts with Blue shorts
Telephone Nº: (01905) 23003
Fax Number: (01905) 26668
Ground Capacity: 4,005
Seating Capacity: 1,100
Web site: www.worcestercityfc.co.uk

GENERAL INFORMATION

Supporters Club: P. Gardner, c/o Club
Telephone Nº: –
Car Parking: Street parking
Coach Parking: Street parking
Nearest Railway Station: Foregate Street (1 mile)
Nearest Bus Station: Crowngate Bus Station
Club Shop: At the ground
Opening Times: Matchdays only 10.00am – 5.00pm
Telephone Nº: (01905) 23003
Police Telephone Nº: (01905) 723888

GROUND INFORMATION

Away Supporters' Entrances & Sections:
Turnstile at the Canal End when segregation in in force for
Canal End accommodation

ADMISSION INFO (2005/2006 PRICES)

Adult Standing: £9.00
Adult Seating: £10.00
Child/Senior Citizen Standing: £5.00
Child/Senior Citizen Seating: £6.00
Programme Price: £2.00

DISABLED INFORMATION

Wheelchairs: 3 covered spaces available
Helpers: Please phone the club for information
Prices: Please phone the club for information
Disabled Toilets: None
Contact: (01905) 23003   (Bookings are necessary)

Travelling Supporters' Information:
Routes: Exit the M5 at Junction 6 and take the A449 Kidderminster Road. Follow to the end of the dual carriageway and take the second exit at the roundabout for Worcester City Centre. At the first set of traffic lights turn right into the town centre. The 3rd turning on the left is St. Georges Lane.

WORKINGTON AFC

Founded: 1884 (Reformed 1921)
Former Names: None
Nickname: 'Reds'
Ground: Borough Park, Workington   CA14 2DT
Record Attendance: 21,000 (vs Manchester United)
Pitch Size: 110 × 71 yards

Colours: Red shirts and shorts
Telephone Nº: (01900) 602871
Fax Number: (01900) 67432
Ground Capacity: 2,500
Seating Capacity: 300
Web site: www.workingtonafc.co.uk

GENERAL INFORMATION

Supporters Club: Yes
Car Parking: Car Park next to the ground
Coach Parking: At the ground
Nearest Railway Station: Workington (¼ mile)
Nearest Bus Station: Workington (½ mile)
Club Shop: At the ground
Opening Times: Matchdays only
Telephone Nº: (01946) 832710

GROUND INFORMATION

Away Supporters' Entrances & Sections:
No usual segregation

ADMISSION INFO (2005/2006 PRICES)

Adult Standing: £8.00
Adult Seating: £8.00
Senior Citizen/Junior Standing: £4.00
Senior Citizen/Junior Seating: £4.00
Programme Price: £1.50

DISABLED INFORMATION

Wheelchairs: Accommodated
Helpers: Admitted
Prices: Normal prices apply
Disabled Toilets: Available
Contact: (01900) 602871   (Bookings are not necessary)

Travelling Supporters' Information:
Routes: Exit the M6 at Junction 40 and take the A66 towards Keswick and Workington. Upon reaching Workington, continue until you reach the traffic lights at a T-junction. Turn right here onto the A596 for Maryport. After approximately ½ mile you will see the ground floodlights on the opposite site of the river (to the left). Continue along the A596, pass under the bridge taking the next right signposted for the Stadium. The ground is then on the left hand side opposite the Tesco superstore.

WORKSOP TOWN FC

Founded: 1861   (Reformed in 1893)
Former Names: None
Nickname: 'The Tigers'
Ground: Babbage Way, off Sandy Lane, Worksop,
Nottinghamshire   S80 1TN
Record Attendance: 2,115
Pitch Size: 110 × 72 yards

Colours: Amber shirts with Black shorts
Telephone Nº: (01909) 501911
Fax Number: (01909) 487934
Ground Capacity: 2,500
Seating Capacity: 1,000
Web site: www.worksoptownfc.co.uk

GENERAL INFORMATION
Supporters Club: c/o Club
Telephone Nº: (01909) 501911
Car Parking: Adjacent to the ground
Coach Parking: Adjacent to the ground
Nearest Railway Station: Worksop (2 minutes walk)
Nearest Bus Station: Worksop (2 minutes walk)
Club Shop: At the ground
Opening Times: Matchdays only
Telephone Nº: (01909) 501911
Police Telephone Nº: (01909) 470999

GROUND INFORMATION
Away Supporters' Entrances & Sections:
No usual segregation

ADMISSION INFO (2005/2006 PRICES)
Adult Standing: £8.00
Adult Seating: £8.00
Child Standing: £4.00
Child Seating: £4.00
Programme Price: £2.00

DISABLED INFORMATION
Wheelchairs: Accommodated
Helpers: Admitted
Prices: £3.00 for the disabled. Helpers charged normal
prices
Disabled Toilets: Yes
Contact: (01909) 501911   (Bookings are not necessary)

Travelling Supporters' Information:
Routes: Exit the M1 at Junction 31 from the North or at Junction 30 from the South and follow signs for Worksop. After reaching
Worksop carry on to the bypass and at the 3rd roundabout (next to Sainsburys) turn off following signs for Sandy Lane Industrial
Estate. The ground is ½ mile on the left.

THE NATIONWIDE FOOTBALL CONFERENCE SOUTH CLUBS

Address

Riverside House, 14B High Street,
Crayford, Kent   DA1 4HG

Phone (01322) 411021   **Fax** (01322) 411022

Clubs for the 2005/2006 Season

Basingstoke Town FC .... Page 52
Bishop's Stortford FC .... Page 53
Bognor Regis Town FC .... Page 54
Cambridge City FC .... Page 55
Carshalton Athletic FC .... Page 56
Dorchester Town FC .... Page 57
Eastbourne Borough FC .... Page 58
Eastleigh FC .... Page 59
Farnborough Town FC .... Page 60
Havant & Waterlooville FC .... Page 61
Hayes FC .... Page 62
Histon FC .... Page 63
Lewes FC .... Page 64
Maidenhead United FC .... Page 65
Newport County FC .... Page 66
St. Albans City FC .... Page 67
Sutton United FC .... Page 68
Thurrock FC .... Page 69
Welling United FC .... Page 70
Weston-Super-Mare FC .... Page 71
Weymouth FC .... Page 72
Yeading FC .... Page 73

BASINGSTOKE TOWN FC

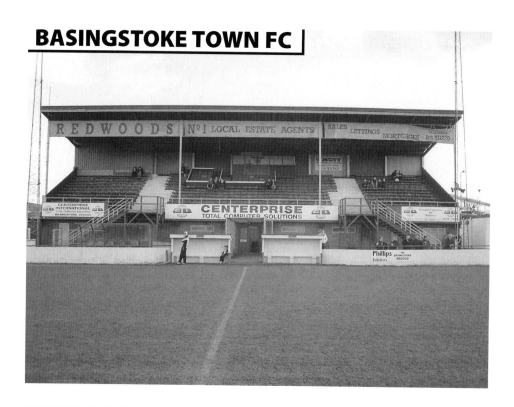

Founded: 1896
Former Names: None
Nickname: 'Stoke' 'Camrose Blues'
Ground: The Camrose Ground, Western Way, Basingstoke, Hants. RG22 6EZ
Record Attendance: 5,085 (25/11/97)
Pitch Size: 110 × 70 yards

Colours: Yellow and Blue shirts with Blue shorts
Telephone Nº: (01256) 327575
Fax Number: (01256) 869997
Social Club Nº: (01256) 464353
Ground Capacity: 6,000
Seating Capacity: 650
Web site: www.btfc.co.uk

GENERAL INFORMATION

Supporters Club: c/o Club
Telephone Nº: (01256) 327575
Car Parking: 600 spaces available at the ground
Coach Parking: Ample room available at ground
Nearest Railway Station: Basingstoke
Nearest Bus Station: Basingstoke Town Centre (2 miles)
Club Shop: The Camrose Shop
Opening Times: Weekdays & Matchdays 10.00am – 5.30pm
Telephone Nº: (01256) 327575
Police Telephone Nº: (01256) 473111

GROUND INFORMATION

Away Supporters' Entrances & Sections:
No usual segregation

ADMISSION INFO (2005/2006 PRICES)

Adult Standing: £9.00
Adult Seating: £10.00
Concessionary Standing: £5.00
Concessionary Seating: £6.00
Under 14's Standing: £2.00
Under 14's Seating: £3.00
Programme Price: £1.50

DISABLED INFORMATION

Wheelchairs: 6 spaces are available under cover
Helpers: Admitted
Prices: Normal prices for the disabled. Free for helpers
Disabled Toilets: Yes
Contact: (01256) 327575 (Bookings are not necessary)

Travelling Supporters' Information:
Routes: Exit the M3 at Junction 6 and take the 1st left at the Black Dam roundabout. At the next roundabout take the 2nd exit, then the 1st exit at the following roundabout and the 5th exit at the next roundabout. This takes you into Western Way and the ground is 50 yards on the right.

BISHOP'S STORTFORD FC

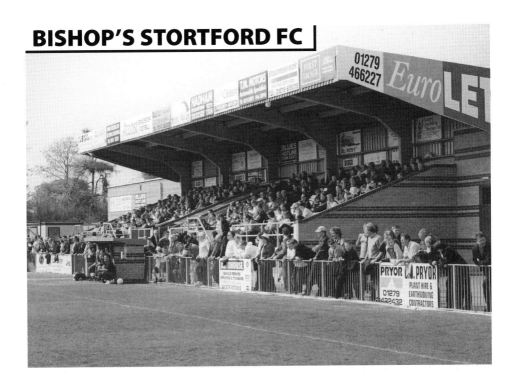

Founded: 1874
Former Names: None
Nickname: 'Blues' 'Bishops'
Ground: Woodside Park, Dunmow Road, Bishop's Stortford CM23 5RG
Record Attendance: 3,555 (2000)
Pitch Size: 110 × 70 yards

Colours: Blue and White shirts with Blue shorts
Telephone Nº: (08700) 339930
Fax Number: (08700) 339931
Ground Capacity: 4,000
Seating Capacity: 298
Web site: www.bsfc.co.uk

GENERAL INFORMATION

Supporters Club: None
Car Parking: 150 spaces available at the ground
Coach Parking: At the ground
Nearest Railway Station: Bishop's Stortford
Nearest Bus Station: Bishop's Stortford
Club Shop: At the ground
Opening Times: Matchdays only 1.30pm to 5.00pm
Telephone Nº: (08700) 339930
Police Telephone Nº: –

GROUND INFORMATION

Away Supporters' Entrances & Sections:
No usual segregation

ADMISSION INFO (2005/2006 PRICES)

Adult Standing: £10.00
Adult Seating: £10.00
Child Standing: £6.00
Child Seating: £6.00
Family Tickets: 1 Adult + 2 Children £18.00;
2 Adults + 2 Children £25.00
Programme Price: £2.00

DISABLED INFORMATION

Wheelchairs: Accommodated in the disabled section
Helpers: Admitted
Prices: Free of charge for the disabled and helpers
Disabled Toilets: Yes
Contact: (08700) 339930 (Bookings are not necessary)

Travelling Supporters' Information:
Routes: Exit the M11 at junction 8 and take the A1250 towards Bishop Stortford. Turn left at the first roundabout and the ground is first right opposite the Golf Club (the entrance is between Industrial Units).

BOGNOR REGIS TOWN FC

Founded: 1883
Former Names: None
Nickname: 'The Rocks'
Ground: Nyewood Lane, Bognor Regis   PO21 2TY
Record Attendance: 3,642 (1984)
Pitch Size: 116 × 75 yards

Colours: White shirts with Green trim, Green shorts
Telephone Nº: (01243) 822325
Fax Number: (01243) 866151
Ground Capacity: 6,000
Seating Capacity: 243
Web site: www.therocks.co.uk

GENERAL INFORMATION
Supporters Club: David Seabourne, c/o Club
Telephone Nº: (01243) 861336
Car Parking: Outside the ground at the Sports Club
Coach Parking: None
Nearest Railway Station: Bognor Regis (1 mile)
Nearest Bus Station: Bognor Regis (1 mile)
Club Shop: At the ground
Opening Times: Matchdays only
Telephone Nº: (01243) 862045
Police Telephone Nº: (0845) 607-0999

GROUND INFORMATION
Away Supporters' Entrances & Sections:
No usual segregation

ADMISSION INFO (2005/2006 PRICES)
Adult Standing: £9.00
Adult Seating: £10.00
Senior Citizen Standing: £6.00
Senior Citizen Seating: £7.00
Child Standing: £2.00
Child Seating: £3.00
Programme Price: £1.50

DISABLED INFORMATION
Wheelchairs: Accommodated
Helpers: Admitted
Prices: Normal prices apply
Disabled Toilets: Available
Contact: (01243) 822325   (Bookings are not necessary)

Travelling Supporters' Information:
Routes: From the West: Take the M27/A27 to Chichester then the A259 and pass through Bersted towards Bognor Regis. Turn right into Hawthorne Road then left into Nyewood Lane – the ground is on the right; From the East: Take the A27 from Brighton/Worthing and turn left onto the A29 at Fontwell Roundabout past Denmans Garden Centre. Travel along Shripney Road and turn right at the second roundabout towards Bersted on the A259 then left into Hawthorne Road – then as above.

CAMBRIDGE CITY FC

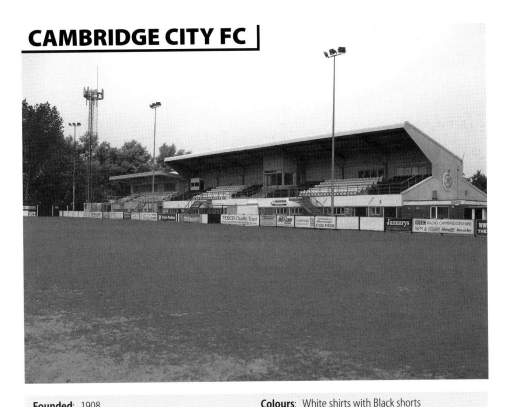

Founded: 1908
Former Names: Cambridge Town FC
Nickname: 'Lilywhites'
Ground: City Ground, Milton Road, Cambridge, CB4 1UY
Record Attendance: 12,058 (1950)
Pitch Size: 110 × 70 yards

Colours: White shirts with Black shorts
Telephone Nº: (01223) 357973
Fax Number: (01223) 351582
Ground Capacity: 3,000
Seating Capacity: 523
Correspondence: Kevin Peters, 9 Villa Court, Cambridge CB4 2TX
Web site: www.cambridgecityfc.com

GENERAL INFORMATION

Supporters Club: Chris Drummond, c/o Club
Telephone Nº: (01223) 357973
Car Parking: 300 spaces available at the ground
Coach Parking: At the ground
Nearest Railway Station: Cambridge (2 miles)
Nearest Bus Station: Cambridge
Club Shop: At the ground
Opening Times: Matchdays only
Telephone Nº: (01223) 357973
Police Telephone Nº: (01223) 358966

GROUND INFORMATION

Away Supporters' Entrances & Sections:
No usual segregation

ADMISSION INFO (2005/2006 PRICES)

Adult Standing: £9.00
Adult Seating: £9.00
Senior Citizen/Under-16s Standing: £4.00
Senior Citizen/Under-16s Seating: £4.00
Under-11s Standing/Seating: £1.00
Family Ticket: 2 adults + 3 children £15.00
Programme Price: £1.50

DISABLED INFORMATION

Wheelchairs: 6 spaces are available under cover on the half-way line
Helpers: Admitted
Prices: Free of charge for the disabled. One helper admitted free with each disabled fan
Disabled Toilets: One available in the Main Stand
Contact: (01223) 357973   (Bookings are not necessary)

Travelling Supporters' Information:
Routes: Exit the M11 at Junction 13 and take the A1303 into the City. At the end of Madingley Road, turn left into Chesterton Lane and then Chesterton Road. Go into the one-way system and turn left into Milton Road (A10) and the ground is on the left behind the Westbrook Centre.

CARSHALTON ATHLETIC FC

Founded: 1905
Former Names: None
Nickname: 'The Robins'
Ground: War Memorial Sports Ground, Colston Avenue, Carshalton   SM5 2PW
Record Attendance: 7,800 vs Wimbledon
Pitch Size: 117 × 76 yards

Colours: White shirts + Maroon Trim, Maroon shorts
Telephone Nº: (020) 8642-8658
Daytime Phone Nº: (020) 8642-8658
Fax Number: (020) 8643-0999
Ground Capacity: 5,000
Seating Capacity: 240
Web site: www.carshaltonathletic.org

GENERAL INFORMATION

Supporters Club: Sylvia Collier, c/o Club
Telephone Nº: (020) 8715-2229
Car Parking: 80 spaces available at the ground
Coach Parking: At the ground
Nearest Railway Station: Carshalton (200 yards)
Nearest Bus Station: 400 yards
Club Shop: At the ground
Opening Times: Matchdays only
Telephone Nº: –
Postal Sales: Yes
Nearest Police Station: Sutton
Police Telephone Nº: (020) 8680-6212

GROUND INFORMATION

Away Supporters' Entrances & Sections:
No usual segregation

ADMISSION INFO (2005/2006 PRICES)

Adult Standing: £9.00
Adult Seating: £10.00
Child Standing: £4.00
Child Seating: £4.50
Programme Price: £1.50

DISABLED INFORMATION

Wheelchairs: 6 spaces each for home and away fans are available at the end of the Main Stand
Helpers: Admitted
Prices: Free for the disabled. Helpers usual prices
Disabled Toilets: Available in the Function Hall
Contact: (020) 8642-8658   (Bookings are necessary)

Travelling Supporters' Information:
Routes: From London: Pick up the A23 at The Elephant & Castle or the Oval. Continue along the Brixton Road (A23), through Brixton up Brixton Hill and continue past Streatham Hill to Streatham High Road (still on the A23). At the traffic lights on the junction at St. Leonard's Church, cross into Mitcham Lane (A216), continue through Streatham Road and bear left at the traffic lights at Figgs Marsh onto London Road (A217) and follow A217 through Bishopsford Road until reaching the Rose Hill roundabout. At the roundabout, take the 1st exit into Wrythe Lane and continue for 1 mile, then turn right into Colston Avenue just before the railway bridge. The ground is 50 yards on the right. A private road leads to the Stadium and car park; From the M25: Exit at Junction 8 onto the A217 passing Lower Kingswood, Kingswood Burgh Heath and Banstead until the roundabout before the sign to Sutton. Bear left, still on the A217 to the Rose Hill roundabout, take the 4th exit, then as above.

DORCHESTER TOWN FC

Founded: 1880
Former Names: None
Nickname: 'The Magpies'
Ground: The Avenue Stadium, Weymouth Avenue, Dorchester, Dorset DT1 2RY
Record Attendance: 4,159 (1/1/99)
Pitch Size: 110 × 80 yards

Colours: Black & White quartered shirts, Black shorts
Telephone Nº: (01305) 262451
Daytime Nº: (01305) 262451 or 262527
Fax Number: (01305) 267623
Ground Capacity: 5,009
Seating Capacity: 710
Web Site: www.the-magpies.net

GENERAL INFORMATION

Supporters Club: H.G. Hill, 39 Thatcham Park, Yeovil, Somerset
Telephone Nº: (01935) 426029
Car Parking: 350 spaces available at the ground
Coach Parking: At the ground
Nearest Railway Station: Dorchester South and West (both 1 mile)
Nearest Bus Station: Nearby
Club Shop: At the ground
Opening Times: During 1st team matchdays only
Telephone Nº: (01305) 262451
Police Telephone Nº: (01305) 251212

GROUND INFORMATION

Away Supporters' Entrances & Sections:
Main Stand side when segregated (not usual)

ADMISSION INFO (2005/2006 PRICES)

Adult Standing: £9.00
Adult Seating: £10.00
Senior Citizen/Child Standing: £5.50
Senior Citizen/Child Seating: £6.50
Under-16s: £1.00 when accompanied by a paying adult
Programme Price: £2.00

DISABLED INFORMATION

Wheelchairs: 10 spaces available each for home and away fans at the North West End of the terracing
Helpers: Admitted
Prices: Normal prices apply
Disabled Toilets: 2 available near the disabled area
Contact: (01305) 262451   (Bookings are not necessary)

Travelling Supporters' Information:
Routes: Take the Dorchester Bypass (A35) from all directions. The ground is on the South side of town, adjacent to a roundabout at the intersection with the A354 to Weymouth. Alternatively, take Weymouth signs from Dorchester Town Centre for 1½ miles.

EASTBOURNE BOROUGH FC

Founded: 1963
Former Names: Langney Sports FC
Nickname: 'The Sports'
Ground: Priory Lane Stadium, Langney Sports Club, Priory Lane, Eastbourne   BN23 7QH
Record Attendance: 1,703
Pitch Size: 115 × 72 yards

Colours: Red shirts with Black shorts
Telephone Nº: (01323) 743561
Fax Number: (01323) 741627
Ground Capacity: 5,644
Seating Capacity: 542
Web site: www.eastbourneboroughfc.co.uk

GENERAL INFORMATION

Supporters Club: Yes – c/o Club
Telephone Nº: –
Car Parking: Around 400 spaces available at the ground
Coach Parking: At the ground
Nearest Railway Station: Pevensey & Westham (1½ miles but no public transport to the ground)
Nearest Bus Station: Eastbourne
Club Shop: At the ground
Opening Times: Matchdays only
Telephone Nº: (01323) 743561
Police Telephone Nº: (0845) 607-0999

GROUND INFORMATION

Away Supporters' Entrances & Sections:
No usual segregation

ADMISSION INFO (2005/2006 PRICES)

Adult Standing: £9.00
Adult Seating: £9.00
Child Standing: £2.50 (Under-16s)
Child Seating: £2.50 (Under-16s)
Senior Citizen Standing: £5.50
Senior Citizen Seating: £5.50
Programme Price: £2.00

DISABLED INFORMATION

Wheelchairs: 6 spaces available
Helpers: Admitted
Prices: Normal prices apply
Disabled Toilets: Available
Contact: (01323) 743561   (Bookings are not necessary)

Travelling Supporters' Information:
Routes: Approaching from the A22: Take the first exit to join the Polegate bypass, signposted A27 Eastbourne, Hastings & Bexhill. *Take the 2nd exit at the next roundabout for Stone Cross and Westham (A22) then the first exit at the following roundabout signposted Stone Cross and Westham. Turn right after ½ mile into Friday Street (B2104). At the end of Friday Street, turn left at the double mini-roundabout into Hide Hollow (B2191), passing Eastbourne Crematorium on your right. Turn right at the roundabout into Priory Road, and Priory Lane is about 200 yards down the road on the left; Approaching from the A27 from Brighton: Turn left at the Polegate traffic lights then take 2nd exit at the large roundabout to join the bypass. Then as from *.

EASTLEIGH FC

Photo courtesy of the Southern Daily Echo

Founded: 1946
Former Names: Swathing Athletic FC, Swathing FC
Nickname: None
Ground: Sparshatts Stadium, Ten Acres, Stoneham Lane, Eastleigh SO50 9HT
Record Attendance: 2,500 (1975)
Ground Capacity: 3,500
Seating Capacity: 350

Pitch Size: 110 × 70 yards
Colours: White shirts with Dark Blue shorts
Ground Telephone Nº: (023) 8061-3361
Correspondence Address: D. Brooks, 2 Highpoint, 50 Midanbury Lane, Bitterne Park, Southampton, SO18 4HF
Contact Telephone Nº: (023) 8055-7147
Web site: www.eastleighfc.net

GENERAL INFORMATION
Car Parking: Spaces for 350 cars available (hard standing)
Coach Parking: At the ground
Nearest Railway Station: Southampton Parkway (¾ mile)
Nearest Bus Station: Eastleigh (2 miles)
Club Shop: At the ground
Opening Times: Matchdays and during functions only

GROUND INFORMATION
Away Supporters' Entrances & Sections:
No usual segregation

ADMISSION INFO (2005/2006 PRICES)
Adult Standing/Seating: £9.00
Senior Citizen Standing/Seating: £5.00
Child Standing/Seating: £2.00
Programme Price: £2.00

DISABLED INFORMATION
Wheelchairs: Accommodated
Helpers: Admitted
Prices: Normal prices apply
Disabled Toilets: Available
Contact: (023) 8061-3361 (Bookings are not necessary)

Travelling Supporters' Information:
Routes: Exit the M27 at Junction 5 (signposted for Southampton Airport) and take the A335 (Stoneham Way) towards Southampton. After ½ mile, turn right at the traffic lights into Bassett Green Road. Turn right at the next set of traffic lights into Stoneham Lane and the ground is on the right after ¾ mile.

FARNBOROUGH TOWN FC

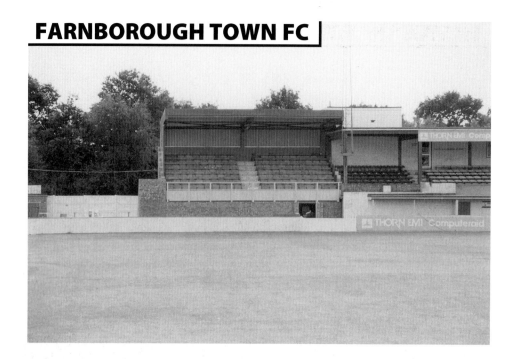

Founded: 1967
Former Names: None
Nickname: 'The Boro'
Ground: Cherrywood Road, Farnborough, GU14 8UD
Record Attendance: 3,581 (1995)
Pitch Size: 115 × 77 yards
Colours: Red and White shirts with Red shorts

Telephone Nº: (01252) 541469
Daytime Phone Nº: (01252) 541469
Fax Number: (01252) 372640
Ground Capacity: 4,163
Seating Capacity: 627
Web site: www.farnboroughtownfc.com

GENERAL INFORMATION
Supporters Club: Bob Perry, c/o Club
Telephone Nº: (01252) 541469
Car Parking: Car Park at the ground
Coach Parking: Adjacent to the ground
Nearest Railway Station: Farnborough (Main), Farnborough North and Frimley
Nearest Bus Station: –
Club Shop: At the ground
Opening Times: Matchdays only
Telephone Nº: –
Police Telephone Nº: (0845) 0454545

GROUND INFORMATION
Away Supporters' Entrances & Sections:
Moor Road entrances and accommodation

ADMISSION INFO (2005/2006 PRICES)
Adult Standing: £10.00
Adult Seating: £12.00
Child Standing: £6.00
Child Seating: £7.00
Senior Citizen Standing: £6.00
Senior Citizen Seating: £7.00
Programme Price: £2.00

DISABLED INFORMATION
Wheelchairs: Spaces in front of the Main Stand
Helpers: Admitted
Prices: Concessionary prices charged
Disabled Toilets: None
Contact: (01252) 541469   (Bookings are not necessary)

Travelling Supporters' Information:
Routes: Exit the M3 at Junction 4 heading for Frimley. At the roundabout take the A331 towards Farnborough. At the traffic lights, turn right into Prospect Avenue and take the 2nd right into Cherrywood Road for the ground.

HAVANT & WATERLOOVILLE FC

Founded: 1998
Former Names: Formed by the amalgamation of Waterlooville FC and Havant Town FC
Nickname: 'The Hawks'
Ground: West Leigh Park, Martin Road, Havant, PO9 5TH
Record Attendance: 3,500 (1985/86)
Pitch Size: 112 × 76 yards

Colours: White shirts and shorts
Telephone Nº: (023) 9278-7822 (Ground)
Fax Number: (023) 9226-2367
Ground Capacity: 5,250
Seating Capacity: 562
Correspondence: Trevor Brock, 2 Betula Close, Waterlooville, PO7 8EJ **Phone**: (023) 9226-7276
Web site: www.havantandwaterlooville.net

GENERAL INFORMATION

Supporters Club: None, but large Social Club
Telephone Nº: (023) 9278-7855
Car Parking: Space for 750 cars at the ground
Coach Parking: At the ground
Nearest Railway Station: Havant (1 mile)
Nearest Bus Station: Town Centre (1½ miles)
Club Shop: At the ground
Opening Times: Daily
Telephone Nº: (023) 9278-7822
Police Telephone Nº: (0845) 454545

GROUND INFORMATION

Away Supporters' Entrances & Sections: Martin Road End

ADMISSION INFO (2005/2006 PRICES)

Adult Standing/Seating: £9.00
Senior Citizen Standing/Seating: £6.00
Under-16s Standing/Seating: £4.00
Note: When accompanied by a paying adult, children under the age of 11 are admitted free of charge
Programme Price: £2.00

DISABLED INFORMATION

Wheelchairs: 12 spaces available in the Main Stand
Helpers: Admitted
Prices: Normal prices for disabled fans. Free for helpers
Disabled Toilets: Two available
Contact: (023) 9226-7276   (Bookings are necessary)

Travelling Supporters' Information:
Routes: From London or the North take the A27 from Chichester and exit at the B2149 turn-off for Havant. Take the 2nd exit off the dual carriageway into Bartons Road and then the 1st right into Martin Road for the ground; From the West: Take the M27 then the A27 to the Petersfield exit. Then as above.

HAYES FC

Founded: 1909
Former Names: Botwell Mission FC
Nickname: 'The Missioners'
Ground: Church Road, Hayes, Middlesex UB3 2LE
Record Attendance: 15,370 (10/2/51)
Pitch Size: 117 × 70 yards

Colours: Red & White striped shirts with Black shorts
Telephone Nº: (020) 8573-2075
Fax Number: (020) 8573-2075
Ground Capacity: 4,300
Seating Capacity: 500
Web site: www.hayesfc.net

GENERAL INFORMATION

Supporters Club: Lee Hermitage, c/o Hayes FC
Telephone Nº: (020) 8573-2075
Car Parking: 300 spaces available at the ground
Coach Parking: By arrangement
Nearest Railway Station: Hayes & Harlington (1 mile)
Nearest Bus Station: Hayes
Club Shop: At the ground
Opening Times: Matchdays only. Saturday matches from 2.00pm–5.00pm. Weekday matches from 6.45pm–9.30pm
Telephone Nº: (020) 8573-5342
Police Telephone Nº: (020) 8900-7212

GROUND INFORMATION

Away Supporters' Entrances & Sections:
Church Road End when segregated (not usual)

ADMISSION INFO (2005/2006 PRICES)

Adult Standing: £9.00
Adult Seating: £10.00
Child/Senior Citizen Standing: £5.00
Child/Senior Citizen Seating: £6.00
Programme Price: £2.00

DISABLED INFORMATION

Wheelchairs: Accommodated as necessary
Helpers: Admitted
Prices: £10.00 for the disabled but a helper is admitted free of charge with each paying disabled fan
Disabled Toilets: Available
Contact: (020) 8573-2075   (Bookings are not necessary)

Travelling Supporters' Information:
Routes: From the A40: Approaching London, take the Ruislip junction – turn right onto the B455 Ruislip Road to the White Hart Roundabout. Take the Hayes bypass to Uxbridge Road (A4020), turn right, then Church Road is ¾ mile on the left, opposite the Adam & Eve pub; From the M4: Exit at Junction 3 and take the A312 to Parkway towards Southall, then the Hayes bypass to Uxbridge Road (A4020). Turn left, then as above.

HISTON FC

Founded: 1904
Former Names: Histon Institute FC
Nickname: 'The Stutes'
Ground: The Glassworld Stadium, Bridge Road, Impington, Cambridge CB4 9PH
Record Attendance: 6,400 (1956)
Pitch Size: 110 × 75 yards

Colours: Red shirts with Black shorts
Telephone N°: (01223) 237373
Fax Number: (01223) 237373
Ground Capacity: 3,750
Seating Capacity: 350
Web site: www.histonfc.co.uk

GENERAL INFORMATION

Supporters Club: Yes
Telephone N°: (01223) 846455 (Jenny Wells)
Car Parking: 250 spaces available at the ground
Coach Parking: For team coaches only
Nearest Railway Station: Cambridge (3 miles)
Nearest Bus Station: Cambridge (3 miles) (Service 107)
Club Shop: At the ground
Opening Times: Saturday matchdays 12.30pm – 6.00pm, Evening matches 6.00pm – 11.00pm
Telephone N°: (01223) 237373

GROUND INFORMATION

Away Supporters' Entrances & Sections:
No usual segregation

ADMISSION INFO (2005/2006 PRICES)

Adult Standing: £8.00
Adult Seating: £10.00
Child Standing: £4.00
Child Seating: £5.00
Programme Price: £1.50

DISABLED INFORMATION

Wheelchairs: Accommodated
Helpers: Please contact the club for details
Prices: The disabled are charged concessionary prices
Disabled Toilets: Available
Contact: (01223) 237373 (Bookings are not necessary)

Travelling Supporters' Information:
Routes: Exit the M11 at Junction 14 and follow the A14 eastwards. Take the first exit onto the B1049 (signposted Histon & Cottenham). Turn left at the traffic lights at the top of the slip road and pass the Holiday Inn on the right. Continue over the bridge and the entrance to the ground is on the right.

LEWES FC

Founded: 1885
Former Names: None
Nickname: 'Rooks'
Ground: The Dripping Pan, Mountfield Road, Lewes BN7 1XN
Record Attendance: 2,500 (vs Newhaven 26/12/47)
Pitch Size: 110 × 72 yards

Colours: Red shirts with Black shorts
Telephone Nº: (01273) 472100
Fax Number: (01273) 472100
Ground Capacity: 3,000
Seating Capacity: 400
Web site: www.lewesfc.com

GENERAL INFORMATION
Supporters Club: c/o Club
Telephone Nº: (01273) 472100
Car Parking: At the ground
Coach Parking: At the ground
Nearest Railway Station: Lewes (adjacent)
Nearest Bus Station: Lewes (½ mile)
Club Shop: At the ground.
Opening Times: Matchdays only

GROUND INFORMATION
Away Supporters' Entrances & Sections:
No segregation

ADMISSION INFO (2005/2006 PRICES)
Adult Standing: £8.00
Adult Seating: £8.00
Junior Standing: £1.00 (Under-16s)
Junior Seating: £1.00 (Under-16s)
Senior Citizen Standing: £4.00
Senior Citizen Seating: £4.00
Programme Price: £1.50

DISABLED INFORMATION
Wheelchairs: Accommodated
Helpers: Admitted
Prices: Normal prices apply for the disabled and helpers
Disabled Toilets: Available
Contact: (01273) 472100

Travelling Supporters' Information:
Routes: From the North: Take the A26 or the A275 to Lewes and follow signs for the Railway Station. Pass the station on the left and take the next left. The ground is adjacent; From the South and West: Take the A27 to the A26 for the Town Centre. Then as above.

MAIDENHEAD UNITED FC

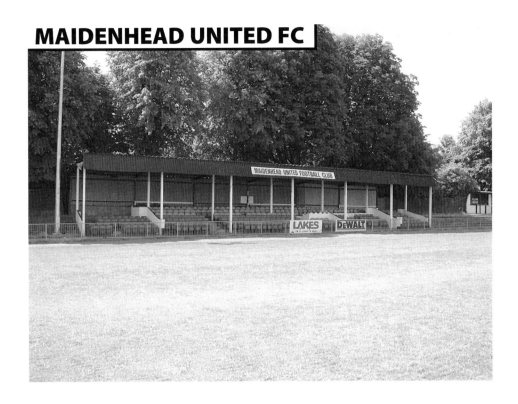

Founded: 1870
Former Names: None
Nickname: 'Magpies'
Ground: York Road, Maidenhead, Berks. SL6 1SF
Record Attendance: 7,920 (1936)
Pitch Size: 110 × 75 yards

Colours: Black and White striped shirts, White shorts
Telephone Nº: (01628) 636314 (Club)
Contact Number: (01628) 636078
Ground Capacity: 4,500
Seating Capacity: 400
Web site: www.maidenheadunitedfc.co.uk

GENERAL INFORMATION

Supporters Club: c/o Club
Telephone Nº: (01628) 620554
Car Parking: Street parking
Coach Parking: Street parking
Nearest Railway Station: Maidenhead (¼ mile)
Nearest Bus Station: Maidenhead
Club Shop: At the ground
Opening Times: Matchdays only
Telephone Nº: (01628) 624739
Police Telephone Nº: –

GROUND INFORMATION

Away Supporters' Entrances & Sections:
No usual segregation

ADMISSION INFO (2005/2006 PRICES)

Adult Standing: £8.00
Adult Seating: £8.00
Concessionary Standing and Seating: £4.00
Child Standing and Seating: £1.00 (Under-16s)
Programme Price: £1.50

DISABLED INFORMATION

Wheelchairs: Accommodated
Helpers: Admitted
Prices: Normal prices for the disabled. Free for helpers
Disabled Toilets: None
Contact: (01628) 636078 (Bookings are not necessary)

Travelling Supporters' Information:
Routes: Exit M4 at Junction 7 and take the A4 to Maidenhead. Cross the River Thames bridge and turn left at the 2nd roundabout passing through the traffic lights. York Road is first right and the ground is approximately 300 yards along on the left.

NEWPORT COUNTY FC

Founded: 1989
Former Names: Newport AFC
Nickname: 'The Exiles'
Ground: Newport Stadium, Stadium Way, Newport International Sports Village, Newport   NP19 4PT
Record Attendance: 4,300 (31st March 2004)
Pitch Size: 112 × 72 yards

Colours: Amber shirts with Black shorts
Telephone Nº: (01633) 662262
Fax Number: (01633) 666107
Ground Capacity: 4,300
Seating Capacity: 1,200
Web site: www.newport-county.co.uk

GENERAL INFORMATION
Supporters Club: Bob Herrin, c/o Club
Telephone Nº: (01633) 274440
Car Parking: Space for 500 cars at the ground
Coach Parking: At the ground
Nearest Railway Station: Newport
Nearest Bus Station: Newport
Club Shop: At the ground
Opening Times: Matchdays only
Telephone Nº: (01633) 662262
Police Telephone Nº: (01633) 244999

GROUND INFORMATION
Away Supporters' Entrances & Sections:
No segregation unless specifically required by Police

ADMISSION INFO (2005/2006 PRICES)
Adult Standing: £8.00
Adult Seating: £8.00
Senior Citizen Standing: £5.50
Senior Citizen Seating: £5.50
Juniors: £1.00
Programme Price: £2.00

DISABLED INFORMATION
Wheelchairs: Accommodated
Helpers: Admitted
Prices: Normal prices for the disabled. Free for helpers
Disabled Toilets: Yes
Contact: (01633) 662262   (Bookings are not necessary)

Travelling Supporters' Information:
Routes: Exit the M4 at Junction 24 and take the exit at the roundabout, signposted 'Southern Distributor Road'. Go straight on at the first two roundabouts then turn left at the 3rd roundabout. Carry straight on over the next two roundabouts, pass the Velodrome then turn left between the two Carcraft buildings. Take the 1st turning on the left into the Stadium car park.

ST. ALBANS CITY FC

Founded: 1908
Former Names: None
Nickname: 'The Saints'
Ground: Clarence Park, York Road, St. Albans, Hertfordshire AL1 4PL
Record Attendance: 9,757 (27/2/26)
Pitch Size: 110 × 80 yards

Colours: Shirts are Yellow with Blue trim, Blue shorts
Telephone Nº: (01727) 864296
Fax Number: (01727) 866235
Ground Capacity: 4,500
Seating Capacity: 900
Web site: www.sacfc.co.uk

GENERAL INFORMATION

Supporters Club: Ian Rogers, c/o Club
Telephone Nº: –
Car Parking: Street parking
Coach Parking: In Clarence Park
Nearest Railway Station: St. Albans City (200 yds)
Nearest Bus Station: City Centre (short walk)
Club Shop: At the ground
Opening Times: Matchdays only
Telephone Nº: (01727) 864296
Police Telephone Nº: (01727) 276122

GROUND INFORMATION

Away Supporters' Entrances & Sections:
Hatfield Road End when matches are segregated

ADMISSION INFO (2005/2006 PRICES)

Adult Standing: £8.00
Adult Seating: £9.50
Under-12s Standing: £3.00   **OAP/Under-16s**: £4.00
Under-12s Seating: £4.50   **OAP/Under-16s**: £5.50
Programme Price: £2.00

DISABLED INFORMATION

Wheelchairs: Accommodated
Helpers: One admitted per disabled supporter
Prices: Free for the disabled, concessionary prices for the helpers
Disabled Toilets: Available inside new Building at the York Road End
Contact: (01727) 864296 (Bookings are not necessary)

Travelling Supporters' Information:
Routes: Take the M1 or M10 to the A405 North Orbital Road and at the roundabout at the start of the M10, go north on the A5183 (Watling Street). Turn right along St. Stephen's Hill and carry along into St. Albans. Continue up Holywell Hill, go through two sets of traffic lights and at the end of St. Peter's Street, take a right turn at the roundabout into Hatfield Road. Follow over the mini-roundabouts and at the second set of traffic lights turn left into Clarence Road and the ground is on the left. Park in Clarence Road and enter the ground via the Park or in York Road and use the entrance by the footbridge.

SUTTON UNITED FC

Founded: 1898
Former Names: Formed by the amalgamation of Sutton Guild Rovers FC and Sutton Association FC
Nickname: 'U's'
Ground: Borough Sports Ground, Gander Green Lane, Sutton, Surrey SM1 2EY
Record Attendance: 14,000 (1970)
Pitch Size: 110 × 72 yards

Colours: Chocolate and Amber striped shirts with Chocolate-coloured shorts
Telephone Nº: (020) 8644-4440
Fax Number: (020) 8644-5120
Ground Capacity: 7,032
Seating Capacity: 765
Web site: www.suttonunited.net

GENERAL INFORMATION

Supporters Club: Tony Cove, c/o Club
Telephone Nº: –
Car Parking: 150 spaces behind the Main Stand
Coach Parking: Space for 1 coach in the car park
Nearest Railway Station: West Sutton (adjacent)
Nearest Bus Station: Sutton
Club Shop: At the ground
Opening Times: Matchdays only
Telephone Nº: (020) 8644-4440
Police Telephone Nº: (020) 8680-1212

GROUND INFORMATION

Away Supporters' Entrances & Sections:
Collingwood Road entrances and accommodation

ADMISSION INFO (2005/2006 PRICES)

Adult Standing: £9.00
Adult Seating: £10.00
Child Standing: £3.00
Child Seating: £4.00
Senior Citizen Standing: £5.00
Senior Citizen Seating: £6.00
Programme Price: £2.00

DISABLED INFORMATION

Wheelchairs: 8 spaces are available under cover accommodated on the track perimeter
Helpers: Admitted
Prices: Normal prices apply
Disabled Toilets: Available alongside the Standing Terrace
Contact: (020) 8644-4440   (Bookings are necessary)

Travelling Supporters' Information:
Routes: Exit the M25 at Junction 8 (Reigate Hill) and travel North on the A217 for approximately 8 miles. Cross the A232 then turn right at the traffic lights (past Goose & Granit Public House) into Gander Green Lane. The ground is 300 yards on the left; From London: Gander Green Lane crosses the Sutton bypass 1 mile south of Rose Hill Roundabout. Avoid Sutton Town Centre, especially on Saturdays.

THURROCK FC

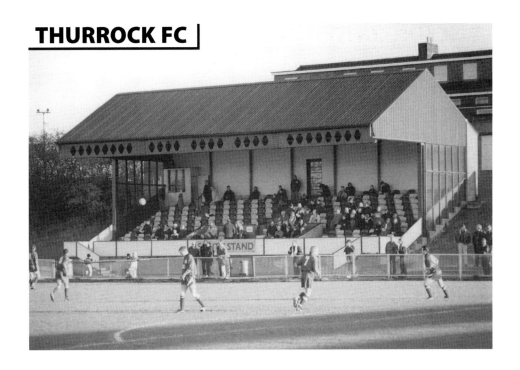

Founded: 1985
Former Names: Purfleet FC
Nickname: 'Fleet'
Ground: Thurrock Hotel, Ship Lane, Grays, Essex, RM15 4HB   **Phone**: (01708) 865492
Record Attendance: 2,572 (1998)
Pitch Size: 113 × 72 yards

Colours: Yellow and Green shirts with Green shorts
Tel Nº: (01708) 868901 (Hotel) or 865492 (Clubhouse)
Contact Nº: (01708) 458301 (Secretary)
Fax Number: (01708) 868863
Ground Capacity: 4,200
Seating Capacity: 500
Web site: www.thurrockfc.com

GENERAL INFORMATION
Supporters Club: None
Car Parking: At the ground
Coach Parking: At the ground
Nearest Railway Station: Purfleet (2 miles)
Nearest Bus Station: Grays Town Centre
Club Shop: At the ground
Opening Times: Matchdays only
Telephone Nº: (01708) 865492
Police Telephone Nº: (01375) 391212

GROUND INFORMATION
Away Supporters' Entrances & Sections:
No usual segregation

ADMISSION INFO (2005/2006 PRICES)
Adult Standing: £9.00
Adult Seating: £9.00
Child Standing: £1.00
Child Seating: £1.00
Senior Citizen Standing: £5.00
Senior Citizen Seating: £5.00
Programme Price: £2.00

DISABLED INFORMATION
Wheelchairs: No special area but accommodated
Helpers: Admitted
Prices: Free for the disabled. Helpers pay normal prices
Disabled Toilets: Available in the Clubhouse
Contact: (01708) 865492   (Bookings are not necessary)

Travelling Supporters' Information:
Routes: Take the M25 or A13 to the Dartford Tunnel roundabout. The ground is then 50 yards on the right along Ship Lane.

WELLING UNITED FC

Founded: 1963
Former Names: None
Nickname: 'The Wings'
Ground: Park View Road Ground, Welling, Kent, DA16 1SY
Record Attendance: 4,020 (1989/90)
Pitch Size: 112 × 72 yards

Colours: Shirts are Red with White facings, Red shorts
Telephone N°: (0208) 301-1196
Daytime Phone N°: (0208) 301-1196
Fax Number: (0208) 301-5676
Ground Capacity: 4,000
Seating Capacity: 500
Web site: www.wellingunited.co.uk

GENERAL INFORMATION

Supporters Club: –
Car Parking: Street parking only
Coach Parking: Outside of the ground
Nearest Railway Station: Welling (¾ mile)
Nearest Bus Station: Bexleyheath
Club Shop: At the ground
Opening Times: Matchdays only
Telephone N°: (0208) 301-1196
Police Telephone N°: (0208) 304-3161

GROUND INFORMATION

Away Supporters' Entrances & Sections:
Accommodation in the Danson Park End

ADMISSION INFO (2005/2006 PRICES)

Adult Standing: £9.00
Adult Seating: £10.00
Senior Citizen/Child Standing: £5.00
Senior Citizen/Child Seating: £6.00
Under-12s: £3.00
Programme Price: £2.00

DISABLED INFORMATION

Wheelchairs: Accommodated at the side of the Main Stand
Helpers: Admitted
Prices: £5.00 for the disabled. Helpers pay normal prices
Disabled Toilets: Yes
Contact: (0208) 301-1196 (Bookings are not necessary)

Travelling Supporters' Information:
Routes: Take the A2 (Rochester Way) from London, then the A221 Northwards (Danson Road) to Bexleyheath. At the end turn left towards Welling along Park View Road and the ground is on the left.

WESTON-SUPER-MARE FC

Founded: 1899
Former Names: Christ Church Old Boys FC
Nickname: 'Seagulls'
Ground: Woodspring Stadium, Winterstoke Road, Weston-Super-Mare BS24 9AA
Record Attendance: 2,623 (vs Woking in F.A. Cup)
Pitch Size: 110 × 70 yards

Colours: White shirts with Blue shorts
Telephone Nº: (01934) 621618
Fax Number: (01934) 622704
Ground Capacity: 3,071
Seating Capacity: 278
Web site: www.westonsupermarefc.co.uk

GENERAL INFORMATION

Supporters Club: Joe Varian, 336 Milton Road, Weston-Super-Mare
Telephone Nº: (01934) 627929
Car Parking: 140 spaces available at the ground
Coach Parking: At the ground
Nearest Railway Station: Weston-Super-Mare (1½ miles)
Nearest Bus Station: Weston-Super-Mare (1½ miles)
Club Shop: At the ground
Opening Times: Matchdays only
Telephone Nº: (01934) 621618
Police Telephone Nº: (01275) 818181

GROUND INFORMATION

Away Supporters' Entrances & Sections:
No usual segregation

ADMISSION INFO (2005/2006 PRICES)

Adult Standing/Seating: £8.50
Senior Citizen Standing/Seating: £5.50
Child Standing/Seating: £3.00
Student Standing/Seating: £3.00 (A valid Student card must be shown)
Programme Price: £1.50

DISABLED INFORMATION

Wheelchairs: Accommodated in a special disabled section
Helpers: Admitted
Prices: Normal prices apply
Disabled Toilets: One available
Contact: (01934) 621618   (Bookings are not necessary)

Travelling Supporters' Information:
Routes: Exit the M5 at Junction 21 and follow the dual carriageway (A370) to the 4th roundabout (Asda Winterstoke). Turn left, go over the mini-roundabout and continue for 800 yards. The ground is on the right.

WEYMOUTH FC

Founded: 1890
Former Names: None
Nickname: 'Terras'
Ground: Wessex Stadium, Radipole Lane, Weymouth, Dorset DT4 9JF
Record Attendance: 4,995 (24/10/87)
Pitch Size: 115 × 74 yards

Colours: Shirts are Claret and Sky Blue, White shorts
Telephone Nº: (01305) 785558
Fax Number: (01305) 766658
Ground Capacity: 6,000
Seating Capacity: 800
Web site: www.theterras.co.uk

GENERAL INFORMATION
Supporters Club: Nigel Beckett, c/o Club
Telephone Nº: (01305) 785558
Car Parking: 200 spaces available at the ground
Coach Parking: At the ground
Nearest Railway Station: Weymouth (2 miles)
Nearest Bus Station: Weymouth Town Centre
Club Shop: At the ground
Opening Times: Matchdays only
Telephone Nº: –
Police Telephone Nº: (01305) 251212

GROUND INFORMATION
Away Supporters' Entrances & Sections:
Visitors End turnstiles and accommodation when segregation is used

ADMISSION INFO (2005/2006 PRICES)
Adult Standing: £9.50
Adult Seating: £10.50
Senior Citizen Standing: £5.00
Senior Citizen Seating: £5.50
Under-15s Seating/Standing: £1.00
Programme Price: £1.80

DISABLED INFORMATION
Wheelchairs: Accommodated
Helpers: Admitted
Prices: Normal prices apply for the disabled. Free for helpers
Disabled Toilets: Yes
Contact: (01305) 785558   (Bookings are not necessary)

Travelling Supporters' Information:
Routes: Take the A354 from Dorchester to Weymouth and turn right at the first roundabout to the town centre. Take the 3rd exit at the next roundabout and follow signs for the ground which is about ½ mile on the right.

YEADING FC

Founded: 1960
Former Names: None
Nickname: 'The Ding'
Ground: The Warren, Beaconsfield Road, Hayes, UB4 0SL
Record Attendance: 3,000 (1990)
Pitch Size: 115 × 72 yards

Colours: Red & Black striped shirts with Black shorts
Telephone N°: (020) 8848-7362
Fax Number: (020) 8756-1200
Ground Capacity: 3,500
Seating Capacity: 250
Web site: www.yeadingfc.co.uk

GENERAL INFORMATION
Supporters Club: –
Car Parking: At the ground
Coach Parking: At the ground
Nearest Railway Station: Hayes (2 miles)
Nearest Bus Station: Uxbridge (2½ miles)
Club Shop: None
Opening Times: –

GROUND INFORMATION
Away Supporters' Entrances & Sections:
No usual segregation

ADMISSION INFO (2005/2006 PRICES)
Adult Standing: £8.00
Adult Seating: £8.00
Senior Citizen/Under-16s Standing: £5.00
Senior Citizen/Under-16s Seating: £5.00
Note: Under-12s are admitted for £1.00 with a paying adult
Programme Price: £1.50

DISABLED INFORMATION
Wheelchairs: Accommodated
Helpers: Admitted
Prices: Normal prices apply
Disabled Toilets: None
Contact: (020) 8848-7362

Travelling Supporters' Information:
Routes: Exit the M4 at Junction 4 and take the A312 past Hayes & Harlington Station. Cross the Grand Union Canal and continue to the Uxbridge Road crossroads. Turn right along Uxbridge Road towards Southall for about ¾ mile then turn right at the traffic lights into Springfield Road then left into Beaconsfield Road. The ground is on the right at the bottom of the road.
Note: Do not approach from the Southall end of Beaconsfield Road – no access to the ground due to the Grand Union Canal!

Nationwide Conference National 2004/2005 Season

	Accrington Stanley	Aldershot Town	Barnet	Burton Albion	Canvey Island	Carlisle United	Crawley Town	Dagenham & Redbridge	Exeter City	Farnborough Town	Forest Green Rovers	Gravesend & Northfleet	Halifax Town	Hereford United	Leigh RMI	Morecambe	Northwich Victoria	Scarborough	Stevenage Borough	Tamworth	Woking	York City
Accrington Stanley		3-3	4-1	3-1	1-0	1-2	4-0	0-3	0-0	2-1	2-2	1-2	1-1	2-1	2-1	2-1	5-0	2-1	4-1	2-3	0-0	2-2
Aldershot Town	0-0		2-3	3-0	2-0	0-5	1-0	4-0	2-1	3-1	1-2	1-0	0-0	0-2	2-0	3-3	2-1	2-0	0-1	4-3	4-0	2-0
Barnet	3-0	2-1		2-3	1-0	1-1	3-0	5-0	1-0	7-1	3-1	4-1	3-1	0-2	3-2	5-1	4-0	1-0	2-1	0-3	2-2	4-0
Burton Albion	2-2	1-3	1-1		1-1	0-1	1-0	1-3	1-0	0-0	4-1	3-2	2-2	3-0	0-0	1-3	1-0	2-3	0-3	1-1	0-1	0-2
Canvey Island	0-2	2-2	0-1	2-2		0-3	2-2	4-2	2-2	1-1	2-1	1-1	0-1	0-4	3-0	0-0	2-2	1-0	3-0	3-3	2-2	4-0
Carlisle United	2-0	1-1	1-3	0-0	0-0		1-0	1-0	0-2	7-0	0-1	2-2	1-0	3-1	3-0	3-3	1-0	2-1	1-2	2-1	2-1	6-0
Crawley Town	2-0	1-0	1-3	4-0	2-1	1-0		2-0	0-1	2-0	4-2	1-1	1-2	1-1	2-2	2-1	0-0	2-1	1-2	3-0	2-1	1-0
Dagenham & Redbridge	0-5	3-0	2-0	3-1	3-1	1-0	1-0		2-3	0-0	2-2	5-0	4-2	3-1	2-0	2-1	2-3	0-3	3-1	0-0	1-1	0-3
Exeter City	1-2	3-1	0-3	3-1	0-1	0-0	3-2	1-1		2-1	2-0	3-0	2-1	4-0	5-1	1-1	2-3	3-1	2-0	2-2	0-0	0-1
Farnborough Town	2-1	1-2	0-0	1-3	1-3	1-2	2-3	2-1	2-1		1-1	0-3	3-2	0-6	0-1	1-2	0-2	0-1	0-3	2-2	0-0	1-1
Forest Green Rovers	1-0	0-0	0-2	3-2	2-2	0-3	1-1	1-4	2-3	1-1		1-5	0-0	1-3	1-1	0-3	1-3	0-1	1-1	1-1	1-3	1-1
Gravesend & Northfleet	2-2	1-3	1-3	0-2	3-2	1-3	0-0	2-1	1-1	2-2	0-0		0-3	1-2	4-1	1-2	2-2	4-0	2-1	2-0	1-1	4-0
Halifax Town	1-2	2-0	2-3	2-0	4-1	2-2	1-0	2-2	2-1	2-0	4-0	1-0		0-1	5-1	1-3	2-2	2-1	2-1	3-3	3-1	2-0
Hereford United	0-0	2-0	1-1	0-0	1-0	0-0	0-0	0-1	1-2	3-1	2-1	1-0	2-3		3-0	1-1	4-0	1-0	0-1	2-1	2-2	2-0
Leigh RMI	0-6	3-3	0-3	1-4	2-1	1-6	1-2	0-1	0-1	1-2	2-0	0-1	0-3	3-4		0-2	0-1	1-1	1-2	2-3	0-3	0-3
Morecambe	1-2	0-0	1-1	3-0	4-0	1-1	1-2	1-0	2-2	1-1	3-1	1-3	2-1	2-1	2-1		3-1	2-1	1-3	3-0	2-1	2-1
Northwich Victoria	3-3	1-2	2-0	4-0	3-1	2-2	1-0	2-2	1-2	2-0	2-1	1-2	1-2	1-4	2-0	2-2		1-0	1-1	1-2	1-3	3-0
Scarborough	4-0	2-2	1-1	1-1	1-1	1-1	2-2	2-0	1-0	4-0	0-0	1-0	3-1	0-0	3-0	1-1	3-0		3-3	2-2	2-0	5-1
Stevenage Borough	5-0	0-1	2-1	0-1	1-4	2-1	1-0	1-0	3-2	3-1	2-2	2-0	2-1	0-1	2-0	0-1	4-1	1-0		2-0	0-2	2-2
Tamworth	1-0	1-2	0-2	0-2	1-0	1-0	1-0	0-4	1-2	0-2	4-0	2-1	2-1	2-2	0-1	0-0	3-0	1-0	0-0		1-3	1-0
Woking	2-1	1-2	1-1	1-0	1-0	1-1	2-0	2-4	3-3	2-0	0-1	2-0	1-1	1-0	0-0	2-0	1-1	1-2	2-1	2-1		1-0
York City	0-1	0-2	2-1	1-2	0-0	2-1	3-1	0-0	1-2	4-0	1-3	0-0	1-1	0-3	1-1	1-0	0-0	0-2	3-1	2-0	0-2	

Nationwide Conference National

Season 2004/2005

Team	P	W	D	L	F	A	Pts
Barnet	42	26	8	8	90	44	86
Hereford United	42	21	11	10	68	41	74
Carlisle United	42	20	13	9	74	37	73
Aldershot Town	42	21	10	11	68	52	73
Stevenage Borough	42	22	5	15	65	52	72
Exeter City	42	20	11	11	71	50	71
Morecambe	42	19	14	9	69	50	71
Woking	42	18	14	10	58	45	68
Halifax Town	42	19	9	14	74	56	66
Accrington Stanley	42	18	11	13	72	58	65
Dagenham & Redbridge	42	19	8	15	68	60	65
Crawley Town	42	16	9	17	50	50	57
Scarborough	42	14	14	14	60	46	56
Gravesend & Northfleet	42	13	11	18	58	64	50
Tamworth	42	14	11	17	53	63	50
Burton Albion	42	13	11	18	50	66	50
York City	42	11	10	21	39	66	43
Canvey Island	42	9	15	18	53	65	42
Northwich Victoria	42	14	10	18	58	72	42
Forest Green Rovers	42	6	15	21	41	81	33
Farnborough Town	42	6	11	25	35	89	29
Leigh RMI	42	4	6	32	31	98	18

Northwich Victoria had 10 points deducted.
Tamworth had 3 points deducted.

Promotion Play-offs

Aldershot Town .... 1 — Carlisle United 0
Stevenage Borough .... 1 — Hereford United 1

Carlisle United .... 2 — Aldershot Town .... 1 (aet)
Carlisle United won 5-4 on penalties
Hereford United .... 0 — Stevenage Borough 1
Stevenage Borough won 2-1 on aggregate

Carlisle United .... 1 — Stevenage Borough 0

Promoted: Barnet and Carlisle United
Relegated: Northwich Victoria, Farnborough Town and Leigh RMI

Nationwide Conference North 2004/2005 Season

	Alfreton Town	Altrincham	Ashton United	Barrow	Bradford Park Avenue	Droylsden	Gainsborough Trinity	Harrogate Town	Hinckley United	Hucknall Town	Kettering Town	Lancaster City	Moor Green	Nuneaton Borough	Redditch United	Runcorn FC Halton	Southport	Stafford Rangers	Stalybridge Celtic	Vauxhall Motors	Worcester City	Worksop Town
Alfreton Town		0-2	1-1	1-1	2-1	0-1	0-1	2-0	0-2	0-2	1-2	2-3	2-2	2-0	1-2	4-0	2-1	0-1	1-0	3-1	0-0	0-0
Altrincham	1-2		1-2	2-0	0-0	2-2	4-1	3-0	4-1	1-1	3-3	4-0	0-2	1-0	0-0	3-3	2-1	1-0	4-1	3-1	2-0	4-1
Ashton United	3-1	0-1		1-2	0-0	1-0	1-3	3-2	0-2	0-0	0-2	2-0	1-3	2-3	2-3	5-4	0-3	1-2	2-3	0-2	1-0	2-3
Barrow	0-3	2-0	1-1		3-2	1-3	2-0	1-0	3-0	0-3	2-1	2-2	3-4	1-3	1-6	1-1	0-2	2-2	2-1	1-2	2-2	2-1
Bradford Park Avenue	0-4	1-2	3-3	0-1		0-2	0-3	1-2	1-1	2-4	1-2	1-0	1-1	2-2	0-3	0-1	3-1	3-1	0-1	0-1	0-1	1-1
Droylsden	3-2	2-0	4-0	2-0	3-3		2-1	2-1	1-0	3-1	2-3	3-4	2-2	1-0	1-0	3-0	1-3	4-0	0-0	4-0	2-3	1-3
Gainsborough Trinity	1-2	0-1	1-0	1-0	2-0	1-1		0-0	1-1	0-1	1-1	4-2	1-1	1-2	2-1	2-3	1-0	1-1	2-2	1-2	3-0	1-1
Harrogate Town	2-1	1-1	5-1	2-1	2-1	2-1	5-1		1-1	0-0	2-1	1-1	1-2	3-1	4-2	1-0	2-5	0-1	2-0	2-1	2-0	0-0
Hinckley United	1-0	2-1	3-1	1-0	4-0	3-3	3-1	0-1		0-3	0-1	2-2	1-2	1-0	0-0	0-2	1-1	1-4	0-4	3-1	0-4	3-1
Hucknall Town	4-0	4-2	2-1	1-2	0-0	0-4	2-5	1-1	1-1		2-1	0-1	1-1	1-3	2-0	1-0	2-4	0-5	0-1	2-0	1-1	2-2
Kettering Town	1-1	0-1	0-0	2-0	1-0	0-2	0-1	0-0	3-1	3-1		0-2	1-2	1-0	1-0	2-1	0-5	0-1	2-0	1-1	2-1	2-1
Lancaster City	0-1	1-1	2-0	2-1	0-1	0-1	2-0	0-3	2-3	2-2	1-0		3-1	0-2	0-0	2-1	1-1	1-0	3-1	0-2	1-0	1-0
Moor Green	0-1	2-2	2-0	1-1	1-0	1-2	2-1	2-1	1-1	1-2	0-2	1-0		1-3	1-0	2-3	0-1	2-2	0-2	1-2	2-0	1-1
Nuneaton Borough	1-1	0-0	1-0	1-1	2-1	3-2	1-0	2-0	0-1	1-3	2-0	2-0	1-0		0-1	3-0	0-1	4-3	1-0	2-1	2-0	0-2
Redditch United	1-3	0-1	3-2	2-0	3-1	1-1	0-1	2-1	3-0	1-1	2-3	0-0	3-1	1-5		1-0	3-2	1-0	2-3	4-1	0-4	3-2
Runcorn FC Halton	1-0	2-1	2-0	1-0	2-1	1-3	0-1	0-0	1-2	1-2	2-0	2-2	2-1	0-2	0-1		0-2	3-3	1-1	1-1	2-2	0-1
Southport	3-1	2-1	1-2	1-0	1-0	3-0	2-1	2-3	3-2	1-0	1-3	0-0	2-1	3-0	1-1	3-1		0-0	1-1	2-1	2-2	1-1
Stafford Rangers	3-1	0-1	1-1	2-2	1-0	2-0	2-0	1-1	1-1	1-2	3-0	2-2	2-1	2-3	1-1	0-0	1-1		3-2	1-1	0-0	4-0
Stalybridge Celtic	2-3	1-1	2-1	1-2	1-4	1-3	2-2	1-3	0-2	1-1	1-2	2-2	2-2	1-1	1-0	3-5	1-0	1-0		2-1	1-0	2-2
Vauxhall Motors	2-0	2-0	0-0	0-2	1-0	1-2	1-0	1-1	0-2	3-1	1-0	1-1	1-1	1-2	0-3	0-0	1-2	0-2	1-0		2-2	1-1
Worcester City	0-0	2-1	2-2	0-1	2-1	3-1	1-2	1-2	1-1	3-0	2-2	3-1	4-1	0-2	2-1	2-1	1-3	0-0	2-1	1-0		0-2
Worksop Town	3-2	1-1	3-1	2-1	2-1	0-2	1-3	2-0	3-1	2-1	0-3	2-0	1-0	2-3	5-3	1-1	1-2	0-1	1-1	2-3	2-0	

Nationwide Conference North

Season 2004/2005

	P	W	D	L	F	A	Pts
Southport	42	25	9	8	83	45	84
Nuneaton Borough	42	25	6	11	68	45	81
Droylsden	42	24	7	11	82	52	79
Kettering Town	42	21	7	14	56	50	70
Altrincham	42	19	12	11	66	46	69
Harrogate Town	42	19	11	12	62	49	68
Worcester City	42	16	12	14	59	53	60
Stafford Rangers	42	14	17	11	52	44	59
Redditch United	42	18	8	16	65	59	59
Hucknall Town	42	15	14	13	59	57	59
Gainsborough Trinity	42	16	9	17	55	55	57
Hinckley United	42	15	11	16	55	62	56
Lancaster City	42	14	12	16	51	59	54
Alfreton Town	42	15	8	19	53	55	53
Vauxhall Motors	42	14	11	17	48	57	53
Barrow	42	14	10	18	50	64	52
Worksop Town	42	16	12	14	59	59	50
Moor Green	42	13	10	19	55	64	49
Stalybridge Celtic	42	12	12	18	52	70	48
Runcorn FC Halton	42	10	12	20	44	63	42
Ashton United	42	8	9	25	46	79	33
Bradford Park Avenue	42	5	9	28	37	70	24

Worksop Town had 10 points deducted.
Redditch United had 3 points deducted.

Promotion Play-offs North

Droylsden .... 1 — Kettering Town 2
Nuneaton Borough .... 1 — Altrincham .... 1 (aet)
Altrincham won 4-2 on penalties

Kettering Town .... 2 — Altrincham .... 3 (aet)

Promotion Play-off North vs South Final

Altrincham .... 2 — Eastbourne Borough 1

Promoted from Conference North: Southport and Altrincham

Nationwide Conference South 2004/2005 Season	Basingstoke Town	Bishop's Stortford	Bognor Regis Town	Cambridge City	Carshalton Athletic	Dorchester Town	Eastbourne Borough	Grays Athletic	Havant & Waterlooville	Hayes	Hornchurch	Lewes	Maidenhead United	Margate	Newport County	Redbridge	St. Albans City	Sutton United	Thurrock	Welling United	Weston-super-Mare	Weymouth
Basingstoke Town	■	2-3	2-1	2-1	0-1	2-2	0-2	0-3	3-2	2-0	2-0	0-0	0-1	2-1	3-0	3-0	5-1	1-0	3-0	4-0	1-1	0-1
Bishop's Stortford	1-3	■	2-3	3-0	2-0	2-1	2-0	1-2	1-1	0-4	3-1	1-0	2-1	3-0	3-0	2-1	2-0	3-2	0-0	4-2	2-2	0-2
Bognor Regis Town	2-1	3-1	■	1-2	1-0	7-2	1-0	0-0	1-1	1-2	3-1	1-3	1-2	2-2	0-2	4-1	4-1	0-1	3-2	6-5	3-0	2-2
Cambridge City	2-1	3-2	1-0	■	3-0	2-2	2-2	0-2	2-0	1-0	0-3	2-3	0-1	2-1	2-0	2-1	0-2	0-1	0-0	0-1	1-2	4-1
Carshalton Athletic	2-0	0-3	0-0	0-2	■	4-3	1-4	0-2	2-1	3-2	0-2	1-0	1-1	0-1	1-0	1-0	1-3	1-2	0-2	0-1	1-1	0-1
Dorchester Town	0-1	4-3	1-0	0-0	1-1	■	3-1	0-7	2-1	1-1	3-1	1-1	4-2	2-0	1-0	4-1	2-3	2-2	0-2	3-2	2-3	4-1
Eastbourne Borough	2-0	1-1	4-1	1-2	1-4	3-2	■	2-2	1-2	1-0	4-2	1-2	0-0	1-1	1-0	1-2	1-0	2-2	4-0	0-1	3-0	4-2
Grays Athletic	0-1	3-0	6-0	1-2	4-0	2-2	1-1	■	3-0	1-1	5-1	4-0	4-0	5-0	0-0	4-1	2-0	5-1	2-1	4-2	2-0	2-0
Havant & Waterlooville	5-1	0-4	0-0	0-2	4-1	4-0	2-1	1-2	■	0-0	4-1	2-1	2-1	3-1	1-0	1-0	1-1	1-2	0-2	2-3	3-2	1-0
Hayes	0-1	2-3	0-1	4-0	1-3	0-1	1-1	1-1	1-5	■	1-1	3-2	2-1	1-0	3-1	1-0	3-2	1-0	1-3	1-1	1-0	1-3
Hornchurch	6-0	3-1	1-1	0-1	2-2	2-3	2-0	1-2	4-0	1-1	■	3-2	6-0	1-0	1-1	2-0	1-1	3-0	0-1	0-5	3-2	2-1
Lewes	0-0	2-1	2-1	2-2	1-1	3-1	1-0	3-2	3-1	3-2	1-2	■	0-1	7-3	2-2	5-4	1-2	0-1	1-1	2-1	3-1	0-0
Maidenhead United	1-1	2-2	2-3	1-5	4-0	0-1	1-2	0-3	1-0	1-1	2-2	1-0	■	2-4	0-2	4-3	3-3	2-2	0-3	2-1	0-0	2-3
Margate	2-1	1-0	2-3	0-2	0-1	1-2	2-1	0-6	5-1	3-1	0-1	1-1	2-0	■	1-1	2-0	2-3	1-1	2-1	1-2	2-0	0-1
Newport County	0-1	6-3	1-0	0-1	0-1	3-2	1-3	1-4	1-1	2-2	2-2	2-1	2-0	■	■	2-3	1-0	2-4	1-2	4-1	2-2	2-0
Redbridge	0-3	1-1	1-2	0-0	1-3	4-1	0-3	1-3	3-1	0-1	0-1	0-1	4-1	2-1	0-5	■	2-1	0-5	1-2	1-2	1-1	3-2
St. Albans City	2-1	2-0	4-0	1-0	3-1	1-1	0-0	1-4	3-1	0-1	4-3	2-3	1-2	3-3	0-1	2-3	■	1-2	1-3	2-5	1-0	0-3
Sutton United	1-0	0-0	0-0	0-3	4-1	3-2	0-0	0-6	1-4	1-2	3-5	2-2	2-0	0-0	2-3	1-2		■	1-2	1-0	1-2	0-3
Thurrock	3-1	1-0	0-5	0-1	2-2	1-2	1-0	2-4	1-3	2-1	1-0	2-0	1-2	1-2	2-2	1-0	1-2	1-2	■	1-1	3-1	2-1
Welling United	0-1	0-0	1-1	0-2	4-0	1-4	0-3	1-2	0-1	1-1	1-1	1-0	1-2	1-0	3-1	1-2	2-3	3-2	1-2	■	1-1	0-1
Weston-super-Mare	2-1	2-1	2-1	2-1	1-1	2-2	0-2	2-0	2-1	0-1	0-0	1-2	2-1	2-2	3-1	1-0	3-0	2-1	2-1	0-2	■	2-2
Weymouth	1-1	3-2	2-1	1-2	2-2	1-1	0-1	1-1	3-2	3-1	2-0	3-3	3-1	2-2	0-1	1-0	1-0	1-1	1-2	0-3	1-1	■

Nationwide Conference South

Season 2004/2005

	P	W	D	L	F	A	Pts
Grays Athletic	42	30	8	4	118	31	98
Cambridge City	42	23	6	13	60	44	75
Thurrock	42	21	6	15	61	56	69
Lewes	42	18	11	13	73	64	65
Eastbourne Borough	42	18	10	14	65	47	64
Basingstoke Town	42	19	6	17	57	52	63
Weymouth	42	17	11	14	62	59	62
Dorchester Town	42	17	11	14	77	81	62
Bognor Regis Town	42	17	9	16	70	65	60
Bishop's Stortford	42	17	8	17	70	66	59
Weston-super-Mare	42	15	13	14	55	60	58
Hayes	42	15	11	16	55	57	56
Havant & Waterlooville	42	16	7	19	64	69	55
St. Albans City	42	16	6	20	64	76	54
Sutton United	42	14	11	17	60	71	53
Welling United	42	15	7	20	64	68	52
Hornchurch	42	17	10	15	71	63	51
Newport County	42	13	11	18	56	61	50
Carshalton Athletic	42	13	9	20	44	72	48
Maidenhead United	42	12	10	20	54	81	46
Margate	42	12	8	22	54	75	34
Redbridge	42	11	3	28	50	86	33

Horchurch and Margate had 10 points deducted.
Redbridge had 3 points deducted.

Promotion Play-offs South

Thurrock 2   Eastbourne Borough 4
Cambridge City qualified for the South Final after Lewes withdrew

Cambridge City 0   Eastbourne Borough 3

Promotion Play-off North vs South Final

Altrincham 2   Eastbourne Borough 1

Promoted from Conference South: Grays Athletic

Unibond League Premier Division 2004/2005 Season	Bamber Bridge	Bishop Auckland	Blyth Spartans	Bridlington Town	Burscough	Farsley Celtic	Frickley Athletic	Gateshead	Guiseley	Hyde United	Leek Town	Lincoln United	Marine	Matlock Town	Ossett Town	Prescot Cables	Radcliffe Borough	Spennymoor United	Wakefield & Emley	Whitby Town	Witton Albion	Workington
Bamber Bridge	■	0-0	1-3	2-1	2-3	1-2	2-0	0-2	2-1	0-4	0-4	2-3	2-1	0-1	3-3	0-2	0-3	1-1	3-2	1-2	1-1	0-2
Bishop Auckland	3-0	■	1-1	2-3	1-2	0-1	2-1	4-3	1-1	0-2	1-3	1-2	2-1	4-1	1-0	1-3	4-0	4-2	1-3	1-1	0-1	0-2
Blyth Spartans	0-1	3-0	■	5-1	2-4	1-4	1-1	2-0	2-2	0-2	0-1	2-0	1-0	1-1	0-1	0-2	2-0	1-0	5-2	2-2	2-1	1-0
Bridlington Town	2-2	2-2	1-1	■	0-1	0-2	1-1	2-1	4-1	1-2	0-0	1-2	1-1	0-2	1-1	2-0	0-3	1-2	1-0	0-0	0-0	0-0
Burscough	4-0	4-0	0-1	0-4	■	1-4	2-1	3-2	3-2	4-0	0-0	7-3	1-3	3-0	5-3	3-5	2-4	5-0	3-3	5-1	1-1	1-3
Farsley Celtic	5-1	2-0	1-1	3-1	1-2	■	2-1	1-0	3-1	2-0	2-3	1-0	0-0	4-0	2-0	0-0	1-1	1-1	5-0	1-2	0-1	0-2
Frickley Athletic	1-0	1-0	2-0	3-1	2-1	2-4	■	1-1	0-1	1-2	0-2	1-0	1-1	1-5	1-1	1-1	2-3	1-1	1-2	1-1	2-1	0-1
Gateshead	2-2	1-1	2-1	2-2	3-3	1-0	1-1	■	2-1	1-3	2-2	2-3	1-3	2-1	3-3	1-1	0-1	5-1	2-1	0-3	2-1	1-1
Guiseley	4-2	5-2	2-1	3-1	3-1	2-2	0-0	1-2	■	1-1	2-1	1-1	1-2	2-4	0-0	2-3	4-3	3-2	1-0	1-1	1-1	1-3
Hyde United	2-1	1-0	3-0	2-1	6-1	2-4	1-1	4-0	3-1	■	1-1	1-1	1-0	2-2	2-0	2-2	3-0	0-0	2-1	2-2	1-0	1-0
Leek Town	4-2	2-1	0-0	2-1	2-0	1-1	1-2	5-0	1-3	2-2	■	0-2	0-2	2-2	2-0	1-1	0-0	0-0	0-0	4-0	2-2	1-1
Lincoln United	2-0	1-2	1-0	2-1	2-3	0-1	3-0	1-2	0-1	1-2	2-3	■	4-1	3-0	2-1	0-3	1-3	0-0	1-2	0-1	1-5	3-2
Marine	3-3	4-1	0-0	1-1	1-1	2-1	1-1	4-2	0-0	2-2	2-2	2-2	■	1-1	3-1	0-2	1-3	0-0	1-2	2-3	1-1	1-2
Matlock Town	3-2	0-2	0-0	0-0	3-1	1-2	1-1	1-1	1-1	1-1	3-2	2-1	1-3	■	1-0	0-1	3-0	2-3	2-1	1-1	1-4	1-2
Ossett Town	2-3	1-1	1-1	5-1	0-0	1-2	2-1	1-0	1-0	2-4	3-0	1-0	3-0	1-1	■	0-2	0-2	4-3	2-1	2-1	1-2	0-1
Prescot Cables	2-1	2-1	2-1	3-2	1-3	1-4	0-2	3-1	0-1	0-1	2-1	1-0	0-0	2-3	2-1	■	2-2	0-0	3-0	0-2	1-1	1-4
Radcliffe Borough	1-2	3-2	1-1	1-1	1-2	0-2	0-0	3-0	1-4	1-0	1-1	1-1	2-2	1-1	2-2	2-1	■	2-2	3-2	0-1	1-1	0-2
Spennymoor United	0-3	5-0	2-3	0-0	2-1	1-0	0-2	2-2	3-3	1-3	0-0	1-0	0-0	0-2	0-0	0-0	0-0	■	5-2	1-0	0-0	1-5
Wakefield Emley	4-0	0-2	3-1	2-0	0-0	2-3	1-0	1-3	1-3	3-3	2-1	3-0	0-0	1-2	2-2	2-1	1-2	3-0	■	0-0	1-0	1-1
Whitby Town	3-0	2-0	4-2	1-0	1-4	2-1	3-1	3-2	2-1	1-1	2-0	1-0	2-1	3-2	1-0	3-2	0-2	0-0	1-2	■	2-2	0-1
Witton Albion	2-0	1-0	2-2	1-0	0-3	2-2	2-1	4-1	0-0	1-1	1-3	1-0	3-0	1-0	0-0	1-3	4-1	1-2	1-1	0-2	■	1-0
Workington	2-0	1-0	1-0	2-1	1-0	1-2	2-1	3-0	1-2	0-2	4-1	1-2	3-0	4-0	3-1	2-0	0-0	5-0	0-0	1-2	1-1	■

Unibond League Premier Division

Season 2004/2005

Team	P	W	D	L	F	A	Pts
Hyde United	42	25	13	4	80	43	88
Workington	42	26	7	9	73	30	85
Farsley Celtic	42	25	8	9	81	41	83
Whitby Town	42	23	11	8	65	49	80
Prescot Cables	42	21	12	9	63	54	75
Burscough	42	21	7	14	93	74	70
Leek Town	42	16	15	11	63	52	63
Witton Albion	42	15	17	10	56	44	62
Radcliffe Borough	42	16	14	12	60	60	62
Guiseley	42	16	13	13	70	64	61
Matlock Town	42	14	13	15	59	67	55
Blyth Spartans	42	13	13	16	53	55	52
Wakefield Emley	42	14	10	18	60	67	52
Lincoln United	42	15	4	23	53	66	49
Marine	42	10	18	14	53	60	48
Ossett Town	42	11	13	18	53	62	46
Gateshead	42	11	12	19	61	84	45
Frickley Athletic	42	10	14	18	44	57	44
Bishop Auckland	42	11	7	24	51	74	40
Bridlington Town	42	7	14	21	43	66	35
Bamber Bridge	42	9	7	26	48	92	34
Spennymoor United	42	9	10	23	44	65	25

Spennymoor United had 12 points deducted.

Promotion Play-offs

Farsley Celtic 1   Whitby Town .... 0 (aet)
Workington 3   Prescot Cables 1

Workington 0   Farsley Celtic .... 0 (aet)
Workington won 6-5 on penalties

Promoted: Hyde United and Workington

Southern League Premier Division 2004/2005 Season

	Aylesbury United	Banbury United	Bath City	Bedford Town	Chesham United	Chippenham Town	Cirencester Town	Dunstable Town	Gloucester City	Grantham Town	Halesowen Town	Hednesford Town	Hemel Hempstead Town	Histon	Hitchin Town	King's Lynn	Merthyr Tydfil	Rugby United	Solihull Borough	Stamford	Team Bath	Tiverton Town
Aylesbury United		2-1	0-1	1-1	2-1	3-2	1-2	5-0	2-0	3-2	1-0	1-4	0-2	1-3	4-3	1-4	2-1	1-2	1-0	1-2	1-2	3-1
Banbury United	1-1		1-3	5-1	2-2	1-3	1-2	1-1	0-0	1-4	1-4	1-0	3-1	1-1	2-1	3-1	1-2	0-0	2-0	2-2	0-4	3-1
Bath City	2-0	2-1		1-4	2-1	1-1	1-0	2-1	1-1	2-0	1-1	3-4	2-0	2-2	4-0	0-3	0-2	0-1	0-1	0-0	0-0	1-0
Bedford Town	2-1	4-2	0-0		2-3	2-1	3-0	0-1	0-0	2-2	3-0	2-1	0-2	3-0	0-0	1-0	2-1	3-1	3-1	2-1	4-1	1-1
Chesham United	1-2	2-3	1-1	0-0		2-3	3-1	8-1	3-2	2-0	0-2	0-2	3-0	2-7	3-1	0-3	1-3	2-3	0-2	5-1	2-0	2-1
Chippenham Town	0-1	3-2	2-4	1-1	2-3		5-0	4-1	3-2	1-1	2-1	0-1	5-2	0-5	1-2	1-0	2-0	1-1	2-1	3-1	1-1	0-0
Cirencester Town	3-0	1-0	2-0	3-0	1-2	0-1		1-1	1-0	5-1	0-5	1-1	3-1	2-0	3-1	1-3	1-1	1-1	4-1	3-0	3-2	0-2
Dunstable Town	2-1	1-2	1-3	3-1	3-2	0-6	0-4		0-2	1-5	4-2	0-3	2-1	0-1	4-1	4-1	2-2	1-3	0-1	1-4	2-0	0-3
Gloucester City	0-3	4-1	2-1	2-2	3-2	0-3	0-0	3-1		1-1	3-3	2-0	2-3	1-2	3-1	2-0	3-3	6-1	0-1	0-0	2-1	1-1
Grantham Town	1-2	3-2	1-0	1-2	2-0	0-2	0-1	2-1	0-0		0-2	2-0	3-1	3-2	2-1	5-1	3-2	0-1	3-1	3-2	0-0	0-1
Halesowen Town	3-1	2-0	0-0	2-1	1-2	3-3	1-1	4-4	0-2	1-0		1-0	2-0	0-2	1-3	1-0	1-0	0-1	4-0	1-1	0-1	3-1
Hednesford Town	0-2	1-0	1-1	1-0	1-2	0-0	3-1	2-1	4-1	0-0	1-2		0-2	4-1	1-2	5-1	1-2	2-1	3-2	2-0	3-1	1-0
Hemel Hempstead Town	2-3	2-4	1-3	0-0	1-2	1-1	1-2	1-0	2-2	2-2	0-2	0-6		3-2	2-3	2-0	1-2	4-3	2-1	2-1	1-1	0-0
Histon	2-0	3-1	5-1	3-3	2-1	1-0	2-2	3-1	0-1	2-1	3-1	1-1	2-1		2-3	3-2	1-2	1-2	3-0	3-0	0-2	3-1
Hitchin Town	1-4	1-0	0-1	1-4	2-2	0-1	0-0	1-5	1-1	0-1	1-1	2-1	1-4	0-3		3-0	0-2	4-2	3-1	0-0	3-1	0-1
King's Lynn	1-0	1-0	0-2	2-0	5-1	2-3	3-1	4-0	1-0	1-2	0-1	0-0	6-3	1-4	1-2		1-1	4-3	7-3	4-0	4-1	1-1
Merthyr Tydfil	2-0	0-0	0-1	1-1	3-3	3-2	1-0	0-0	2-2	1-0	1-2	0-2	0-0	0-3	1-1	5-1		2-1	2-0	1-1	3-2	1-1
Rugby United	1-2	0-1	0-0	0-1	2-1	1-2	0-0	2-2	2-0	0-1	1-1	0-0	1-1	1-4	2-0	2-0	0-2		1-0	1-1	0-0	1-1
Solihull Borough	0-3	0-2	0-4	0-4	1-2	0-2	1-1	0-1	3-3	1-0	3-1	0-4	5-0	1-3	2-0	0-1	1-2	0-2		1-0	0-1	3-3
Stamford	1-1	0-0	0-0	0-2	5-0	1-2	1-2	1-0	0-0	1-0	1-2	1-1	2-2	1-1	2-2	1-2	0-0	1-0	3-3		1-1	0-1
Team Bath	3-1	3-1	1-4	3-2	1-4	1-3	0-2	3-2	1-1	1-0	2-0	0-0	3-3	2-0	1-1	0-5	1-2	2-1	0-3	1-0		1-1
Tiverton Town	4-3	0-1	2-0	3-1	1-6	3-1	2-2	3-1	5-3	3-0	1-0	1-1	3-1	3-2	1-3	1-1	0-1	5-0	3-1	2-0	2-2	

Southern League Premier Division

Season 2004/2005

Histon	42	24	6	12	93	57	78
Chippenham Town	42	22	9	11	81	55	75
Merthyr Tydfil	42	19	14	9	62	47	71
Hednesford Town	42	20	10	12	68	40	70
Bedford Town	42	19	12	11	70	52	69
Bath City	42	19	12	11	57	43	69
Cirencester Town	42	19	11	12	63	52	68
Tiverton Town	42	18	13	11	70	55	67
Halesowen Town	42	19	9	14	64	52	66
Aylesbury United	42	20	3	19	67	66	63
King's Lynn	42	19	4	19	78	69	61
Chesham United	42	18	5	19	84	82	59
Grantham Town	42	17	7	18	57	55	58
Team Bath	42	14	12	16	54	68	54
Gloucester City	42	12	17	13	63	61	53
Rugby United	42	13	12	17	48	60	51
Banbury United	42	13	9	20	56	69	48
Hitchin Town	42	13	9	20	55	77	48
Hemel Hempstead Town	42	11	10	21	60	88	43
Dunstable Town	42	11	6	25	56	98	39
Stamford	42	6	18	18	40	60	36
Solihull Borough	42	10	4	28	45	85	34

Promotion Play-offs

Chippenham Town 2   Bedford Town .... 2 (aet)
Chippenham Town won 5-4 on penalties
Merthyr Tydfil 1   Hednesford Town .... 1 (aet)
Hednesford Town won 5-3 on penalties

Chippenham Town 0   Hednesford Town 1

Promoted: Histon and Hednesford Town

Rymans League Premier Division 2004/2005 Season

	Billericay Town	Braintree Town	Chelmsford City	Cheshunt	Dover Athletic	Eastleigh	Folkestone Invicta	Hampton & Richmond	Harrow Borough	Hendon	Heybridge Swifts	Kingstonian	Leyton	Northwood	Salisbury City	Slough Town	Staines Town	Tonbridge Angels	Wealdstone	Windsor & Eton	Worthing	Yeading
Billericay Town	■	1-0	1-2	4-1	2-0	2-0	0-0	2-0	1-0	1-1	4-1	6-1	0-3	2-1	0-0	2-0	2-1	1-1	2-0	2-1	0-0	1-1
Braintree Town	5-0	■	1-1	1-2	1-1	1-1	0-0	3-1	2-0	1-0	3-0	5-1	2-0	0-0	2-2	2-1	1-2	0-0	1-0	1-0	3-0	0-0
Chelmsford City	1-3	1-1	■	2-2	5-2	2-2	2-1	2-1	1-0	0-1	5-2	3-2	3-5	1-0	1-3	3-0	1-2	2-1	1-0	0-1	2-1	1-2
Cheshunt	3-2	0-3	0-3	■	5-2	2-4	0-0	0-0	0-0	2-1	2-1	1-5	0-0	2-2	2-2	1-0	0-3	1-1	0-1	1-1	1-0	1-2
Dover Athletic	1-1	1-3	1-1	2-1	■	1-2	0-1	2-0	2-2	0-1	1-2	1-2	2-2	0-1	2-1	3-1	3-1	2-1	2-4	1-0	1-2	0-3
Eastleigh	1-1	0-0	3-0	1-0	1-0	■	1-1	3-3	1-1	7-1	1-0	6-3	1-0	4-2	3-0	0-4	4-0	2-0	1-2	0-0	3-0	1-1
Folkestone Invicta	1-0	2-2	1-0	4-3	1-0	2-2	■	0-2	1-0	0-1	1-3	3-0	2-1	0-0	3-1	3-1	0-3	2-0	3-0	2-2	1-2	1-2
Hampton & Richmond	0-3	0-0	1-1	2-1	1-0	5-1	2-1	■	2-0	1-0	1-2	2-1	2-1	1-0	3-2	2-2	2-0	2-2	2-1	2-1	2-1	2-1
Harrow Borough	0-3	1-1	1-1	1-3	1-4	1-2	1-0	1-0	■	1-3	1-2	2-2	2-1	1-1	3-2	1-2	1-0	1-0	2-1	1-1	2-0	1-2
Hendon	1-3	1-3	0-0	2-1	1-0	2-1	2-1	2-1	1-0	■	3-0	1-0	0-0	0-1	1-2	0-0	0-2	0-0	1-4	2-1	0-1	1-2
Heybridge Swifts	0-1	2-1	1-2	2-2	2-1	1-2	2-0	3-1	1-3	5-2	■	3-0	1-2	6-1	1-2	5-2	0-3	0-0	1-1	3-2	0-0	4-1
Kingstonian	1-3	0-1	2-3	0-3	0-0	0-3	1-5	0-1	1-0	3-4	1-2	■	1-2	1-0	0-4	0-4	0-1	1-2	0-0	0-1	1-1	0-1
Leyton	0-6	2-2	2-0	2-1	1-1	2-2	0-4	4-2	1-2	1-0	0-2	3-1	■	3-2	3-2	0-1	1-3	1-0	4-0	4-0	1-0	1-2
Northwood	1-1	1-4	3-1	2-0	1-0	0-3	3-0	2-4	0-0	2-0	2-0	0-1	1-4	■	0-3	1-0	2-0	1-3	2-0	1-3	0-3	2-3
Salisbury City	1-0	0-0	0-2	1-0	0-0	0-0	1-0	2-1	1-2	2-1	1-1	1-0	0-2	1-4	■	0-0	1-3	1-0	3-1	5-1	1-2	1-3
Slough Town	0-6	3-0	0-2	2-0	3-2	1-4	1-1	0-1	2-0	1-3	1-3	2-3	1-2	1-1	1-0	■	1-0	2-0	1-0	3-1	1-1	2-2
Staines Town	3-1	1-1	0-0	1-3	1-3	0-1	0-0	2-0	1-1	1-1	3-2	0-2	3-1	2-2	4-0		■	1-3	3-3	1-3	2-1	0-1
Tonbridge Angels	0-2	2-1	2-1	1-6	3-2	0-3	3-2	3-2	0-0	4-1	0-4	1-1	3-2	2-3	2-3	2-2	0-3	■	0-1	0-1	1-0	1-2
Wealdstone	2-3	2-4	3-2	3-1	0-1	1-4	3-0	2-1	0-3	2-3	2-2	4-5	1-2	1-2	4-2	1-1	3-1	1-1	■	1-1	1-0	2-3
Windsor & Eton	1-1	1-2	0-0	1-3	1-1	1-1	2-1	1-5	2-0	0-1	3-3	1-0	0-0	1-0	2-1	0-4	2-1	4-1	0-0	■	0-2	1-1
Worthing	1-1	0-3	2-2	1-1	1-0	3-0	3-0	0-1	2-1	0-0	2-1	2-0	1-3	1-0	5-1	1-4	0-0	4-0	0-1	1-1	■	2-1
Yeading	3-1	1-1	2-0	3-0	3-2	3-2	1-0	0-0	0-1	3-2	1-1	2-0	1-1	2-0	1-2	3-3	1-2	2-1	2-1	3-2	1-1	■

Rymans League Premier Division

Season 2004/2005

Team	P	W	D	L	F	A	Pts
Yeading	42	25	11	6	74	48	86
Billericay Town	42	23	11	8	78	40	80
Eastleigh	42	22	13	7	84	49	79
Braintree Town	42	19	17	6	67	33	74
Leyton	42	21	8	13	71	57	71
Hampton & Richmond	42	21	8	13	64	53	71
Heybridge Swifts	42	18	9	15	76	65	63
Chelmsford City	42	17	11	14	63	58	62
Staines Town	42	17	9	16	59	53	60
Worthing	42	16	11	15	50	45	59
Hendon	42	17	7	18	48	60	58
Salisbury City	42	16	9	17	60	64	57
Slough Town	42	15	10	17	61	66	55
Folkestone Invicta	42	14	10	18	51	53	52
Windsor & Eton	42	12	14	16	48	62	50
Harrow Borough	42	13	10	19	41	54	49
Northwood	42	14	7	21	49	66	49
Wealdstone	42	13	8	21	60	73	47
Cheshunt	42	12	11	19	58	71	47
Tonbridge Angels	42	11	10	21	47	73	43
Dover Athletic	42	10	9	23	50	66	39
Kingstonian	42	7	5	30	43	93	26

Promotion Play-offs

Billericay Town 0   Leyton 2
Eastleigh 2   Braintree Town 0

Eastleigh 2   Leyton 1

Promoted: Yeading and Eastleigh

79

LDV Trophy 2004/2005

Round	Home		Away		
Round 1	Lincoln City	0	Doncaster Rovers	1	
Round 1	Mansfield Town	0	Darlington	0	(aet)
	Mansfield Town won on penalties				
Round 1	Carlisle United	2	Grimsby Town	1	
Round 1	Hartlepool United	3	Hull City	3	(aet)
	Hartlepool United won on penalties				
Round 1	Hereford United	1	Scunthorpe United	1	(aet)
	Hereford United won on penalties				
Round 1	Huddersfield Town	3	Morecambe	0	
Round 1	Macclesfield	2	Chesterfield	1	
Round 1	Brentford	0	Milton Keynes Dons	3	
Round 1	Notts County	2	Wrexham	3	
Round 1	Port Vale	1	Barnsley	0	
Round 1	Rochdale	4	Scarborough	1	
Round 1	Stockport County	3	Bury	1	(aet)
Round 1	Aldershot Town	0	Wycombe Wanderers	1	
Round 1	Barnet	3	Stevenage Borough	1	
Round 1	Cheltenham Town	5	Dagenham& Redbridge	1	
Round 1	Bristol Rovers	1	Kidderminster Harriers	0	
Round 1	Shrewsbury Town	3	Bournemouth	2	
Round 1	Swansea City	2	Luton Town	0	
Round 1	Torquay United	4	Yeovil Town	3	(aet)
Round 1	Walsall	1	Rushden & Diamonds	0	
Round 1	Woking	0	Leyton Orient	3	
Round 1	Bradford City	1	Accrington Stanley	2	
Round 1	Sheffield Wednesday	1	Chester City	2	
Round 1	York City	0	Blackpool	2	
Round 1	Boston United	0	Cambridge United	1	
Round 1	Bristol City	1	Peterborough United	0	
Round 1	Colchester United	1	Southend United	1	(aet)
	Southend United won on penalties				
Round 1	Oxford United	2	Exeter City	2	(aet)
	Exeter City won on penalties				
Round 2	Blackpool	6	Huddersfield Town	3	(aet)
Round 2	Carlisle United	0	Hartlepool United	1	
Round 2	Chester City	1	Rochdale	0	
Round 2	Hereford United	1	Doncaster Rovers	1	(aet)
	Hereford United won on penalties				
Round 2	Macclesfield	4	Mansfield Town	0	
Round 2	Oldham Athletic	3	Accrington Stanley	2	
Round 2	Tranmere Rovers	2	Port Vale	1	
Round 2	Wrexham	2	Stockport County	0	
Round 2	Bristol City	2	Milton Keynes Dons	1	
Round 2	Cambridge United	0	Leyton Orient	2	
Round 2	Cheltenham Town	2	Walsall	2	(aet)
	Walsall won on penalties				
Round 2	Exeter City	1	Swindon Town	2	
Round 2	Southend United	4	Shrewsbury Town	1	
Round 2	Torquay United	1	Northampton Town	3	
Round 2	Wycombe Wanderers	1	Swansea City	0	
Round 2	Bristol Rovers	2	Barnet	0	

Round 3	Chester City	0	Wrexham	1	
Round 3	Hereford United	2	Blackpool	1	
Round 3	Macclesfield	0	Tranmere Rovers	1	
Round 3	Oldham Athletic	3	Hartlepool United	1	
Round 3	Bristol Rovers	1	Wycombe Wanderers	0	
Round 3	Leyton Orient	1	Walsall	0	
Round 3	Northampton Town	0	Southend United	2	
Round 3	Swindon Town	1	Bristol City	0	
Semi-Final South	Leyton Orient	1	Bristol Rovers	2	
Semi-Final North	Hereford United	1	Wrexham	2	
Semi-Final North	Oldham Athletic	1	Tranmere Rovers	1	(aet)
	Oldham Athletic won on penalties				
Semi-Final South	Southend United	2	Swindon Town	0	

Southern Final

1st leg	Bristol Rovers	1	Southend United	2	
2nd leg	Southend United	2	Bristol Rovers	2	
	Southend United won 4-3 on aggregate				

Northern Final

1st leg	Oldham Athletic	3	Wrexham	5	
2nd leg	Wrexham	1	Oldham Athletic	0	
	Wrexham won 6-3 on aggregate				

FINAL	Wrexham	2	Southend United	0	(aet)

F.A. Trophy 2004/2005

Prelim. Round	AFC Wimbledon	2	Metropolitan Police	0	
Prelim. Round	Arlesey Town	2	Croydon Athletic	1	
Prelim. Round	Ashford Town (Middlesex)	2	Evesham United	1	
Prelim. Round	Barking & East Ham United	2	Fisher Athletic	1	
Prelim. Round	Barton Rovers	2	Wivenhoe Town	3	
Prelim. Round	Bashley	2	Ashford Town	1	
Prelim. Round	Beaconsfield SYCOB	0	Boreham Wood	1	
Prelim. Round	Belper Town	3	Rossendale United	0	
Prelim. Round	Berkhamsted Town	1	Waltham Forest	4	
Prelim. Round	Bromley	2	Chatham Town	1	
Prelim. Round	Bromsgrove Rovers	1	Burnham	0	
Prelim. Round	Burgess Hill Town	2	Wingate & Finchley	1	
Prelim. Round	Clitheroe	1	Kendal Town	4	
Prelim. Round	Corinthian Casuals	2	Banstead Athletic	2	
Prelim. Round	Corby Town	1	Brackley Town	2	
Prelim. Round	Cray Wanderers	3	Aveley	1	
Prelim. Round	Dartford	5	Leatherhead	2	
Prelim. Round	Erith & Belvedere	0	Harlow Town	2	
Prelim. Round	Fleet Town	1	Tilbury	1	
Prelim. Round	Gresley Rovers	4	Spalding United	3	
Prelim. Round	Great Wakering Rovers	1	Maldon Town	0	
Prelim. Round	Hastings United	0	East Thurrock United	3	
Prelim. Round	Horsham	3	Uxbridge	2	
Prelim. Round	Kidsgrove Athletic	4	AFC Telford United	2	
Prelim. Round	North Ferriby United	3	Brigg Town	1	
Prelim. Round	Newport (IOW)	0	Tooting & Mitcham United	2	
Prelim. Round	Sittingbourne	2	Leighton Town	1	
Prelim. Round	Stocksbridge Park Steels	3	Chorley	2	
Prelim. Round	Taunton Town	2	Marlow	1	
Prelim. Round	Thame United	4	Egham Town	2	
Prelim. Round	Warrington Town	2	Ossett Albion	3	
Prelim. Round	Woodley Sports	2	Ilkeston Town	0	
Prelim. Round	Yate Town	2	Swindon Supermarine	0	
Replay	Banstead Athletic	5	Corinthian Casuals	4	(aet)
Replay	Tilbury	2	Fleet Town	1	(aet)
Round 1	Alfreton Town	2	Runcorn FC Halton	0	
Round 1	Altrincham	6	Ossett Albion	1	
Round 1	Arlesey Town	0	Hornchurch	1	
Round 1	Aylesbury United	2	Solihull Borough	1	
Round 1	Bamber Bridge	0	Spennymoor United	0	
Round 1	Banbury United	1	Yate Town	1	
Round 1	Banstead Athletic	2	Wealdstone	3	
Round 1	Bedford Town	2	Stamford	3	
Round 1	Bognor Regis Town	0	Billericay Town	1	
Round 1	Bradford Park Avenue	1	North Ferriby United	1	
Round 1	Bromsgrove Rovers	2	Halesowen Town	1	
Round 1	Bishop Auckland	2	Kidsgrove Athletic	3	
Round 1	Burgess Hill Town	1	Sittingbourne	0	
Round 1	Burscough	2	Guiseley	1	
Round 1	Carshalton Athletic	4	Heybridge Swifts	1	
Round 1	Chesham United	1	Bedworth United	2	
Round 1	Cheshunt	2	Braintree Town	1	
Round 1	Cinderford Town	1	Cambridge City	1	

82

Round 1	Cirencester Town	3	Thame United	2
Round 1	Colwyn Bay	0	Kendal Town	1
Round 1	Cray Wanderers	2	Folkestone Invicta	2
Round 1	Droylsden	1	Leek Town	0
Round 1	Dulwich Hamlet	1	Havant & Waterlooville	1
Round 1	Dunstable Town	2	Histon	6
Round 1	Eastbourne Borough	3	Harrow Borough	1
Round 1	Eastleigh	1	St. Albans City	2
Round 1	Eastwood Town	1	Worksop Town	0
Round 1	Gainsborough Trinity	2	Workington	1
Round 1	Gateshead	1	Southport	1
Round 1	Gloucester City	0	King's Lynn	2
Round 1	Grays Athletic	5	Great Wakering Rovers	1
Round 1	Gresley Rovers	2	Frickley Athletic	1
Round 1	Hampton & Richmond Borough	1	Sutton United	1
Round 1	Hayes	1	Bashley	0
Round 1	Hemel Hempstead	1	Taunton Town	3
Round 1	Hendon	3	AFC Wimbledon	0
Round 1	Hinckley United	3	Stafford Rangers	1
Round 1	Hucknall Town	4	Bracknell Town	0
Round 1	Hyde United	4	Belper Town	1
Round 1	Kingstonian	2	Bishop's Stortford	3
Round 1	Leyton	2	Barking & East Ham United	1
Round 1	Maidenhead United	3	Bromley	4
Round 1	Mangotsfield United	1	Ashford Town (Middlesex)	0
Round 1	Marine	1	Whitby Town	1
Round 1	Matlock Town	2	Lancaster City	2
Round 1	Molesey	1	Welling United	2
Round 1	Moor Green	1	Weymouth	1
Round 1	Mossley	2	Bridlington Town	2
Round 1	Newport County	0	Kettering Town	4
Round 1	Northwood	1	Boreham Wood	4
Round 1	Oxford City	4	Brackley Town	1
Round 1	Paulton Rovers	2	Dorchester Town	3
Round 1	Prescot Cables	1	Lincoln United	1
Round 1	Radcliffe Borough	4	Stocksbridge Park Steels	1
Round 1	Redbridge	5	Dartford	1
Round 1	Redditch United	2	Merthyr Tydfil	1
Round 1	Rocester	2	Ossett Town	1
Round 1	Rothwell Town	2	Nuneaton Borough	1
Round 1	Rugby United	2	Clevedon Town	2
Round 1	Salisbury City	0	Thurrock	4
Round 1	Shepshed Dynamo	0	Willenhall Town	1
Round 1	Slough Town	7	Dorking	0
Round 1	Spennymoor United	4	Bamber Bridge	1
Round 1	Staines Town	2	Dover Athletic	0
Round 1	Stalybridge Celtic	3	Harrogate Town	2
Round 1	Stourport Swifts	0	Sutton Coldfield Town	1
Round 1	Team Bath	3	Hitchin Town	0
Round 1	Tilbury	1	Lewes	4
Round 1	Tiverton Town	0	Bath City	2
Round 1	Tonbridge Angels	3	Horsham	1
Round 1	Tooting & Mitcham United	4	Harlow Town	1
Round 1	Vauxhall Motors (Cheshire)	2	Ashton United	1
Round 1	Wakefield & Emley	2	Farsley Celtic	1
Round 1	Waltham Forest	1	East Thurrock United	1
Round 1	Walton & Hersham	3	Margate	2

Round 1	Weston Super Mare	0	Grantham Town	0	
Round 1	Windsor & Eton	4	Basingstoke Town	0	
Round 1	Witton Albion	2	Blyth Spartans	3	
Round 1	Wivenhoe Town	0	Chelmsford City	3	
Round 1	Woodley Sports	0	Barrow	1	
Round 1	Worcester City	3	Chippenham Town	0	
Round 1	Worthing	1	Whyteleafe	0	
Round 1	Yeading	6	Croydon	1	
Replay	Bridlington Town	4	Mossley	1	
Replay	Cambridge City	3	Cinderford Town	1	
Replay	Clevedon Town	0	Rugby United	1	
Replay	East Thurrock United	1	Waltham Forest	0	
Replay	Folkestone Invicta	1	Cray Wanderers	3	(aet)
Replay	Grantham Town	1	Weston Super Mare	0	
Replay	Havant & Waterlooville	3	Dulwich Hamlet	0	
Replay	Lancaster City	4	Matlock Town	3	(aet)
Replay	Lincoln United	1	Prescot Cables	3	
Replay	North Ferriby United	2	Bradford Park Avenue	2	(aet)
	North Ferriby United won on penalties				
Replay	Southport	2	Gateshead	1	
Replay	Sutton United	4	Hampton & Richmond Borough	1	
Replay	Weymouth	2	Moor Green	1	
Replay	Whitby Town	2	Marine	1	
Replay	Yate Town	3	Banbury United	1	
Round 2	Barrow	3	Rothwell Town	1	
Round 2	Bath City	4	Carshalton Athletic	2	
Round 2	Blyth Spartans	0	Sutton Coldfield Town	3	
Round 2	Boreham Wood	0	Leyton	1	
Round 2	Bridlington Town	0	Eastwood Town	0	
Round 2	Cambridge City	1	Hornchurch	1	
Round 2	Chelmsford City	0	Slough Town	1	
Round 2	Cheshunt	2	Bromley	1	
Round 2	Cray Wanderers	2	St. Albans City	2	
Round 2	Droylsden	2	Spennymoor United	4	
Round 2	East Thurrock United	0	Histon	2	
Round 2	Eastbourne Borough	2	Dorchester Town	1	
Round 2	Gainsborough Trinity	1	Altrincham	1	
Round 2	Grays Athletic	4	Windsor & Eton	1	
Round 2	Gresley Rovers	2	Bedworth United	0	
Round 2	Havant & Waterlooville	2	Grantham Town	1	
Round 2	Hinckley United	1	Willenhall Town	2	
Round 2	Hucknall Town	2	Radcliffe Borough	1	
Round 2	Kendal Town	1	Hyde United	1	
Round 2	Kettering Town	1	Burscough	0	
Round 2	Kidsgrove Athletic	1	Vauxhall Motors (Cheshire)	2	
Round 2	King's Lynn	1	Southport	3	
Round 2	Lancaster City	1	Bromsgrove Rovers	0	
Round 2	Lewes	1	Bishop's Stortford	4	
Round 2	North Ferriby United	1	Alfreton Town	2	
Round 2	Redbridge	1	Weymouth	0	
Round 2	Rugby United	0	Yate Town	1	
Round 2	Staines Town	2	Aylesbury United	3	
Round 2	Stalybridge Celtic	0	Whitby Town	1	
Round 2	Stamford	3	Rocester	1	
Round 2	Taunton Town	0	Hendon	3	
Round 2	Team Bath	4	Wealdstone	2	

Round 2	Thurrock	6	Burgess Hill Town	1	
Round 2	Tonbridge Angels	1	Oxford City	1	
Round 2	Tooting & Mitcham United	2	Hayes	2	
Round 2	Wakefield & Emley	0	Redditch United	1	
Round 2	Walton & Hersham	3	Cirencester Town	2	
Round 2	Welling United	0	Sutton United	1	
Round 2	Worcester City	2	Prescot Cables	1	
Round 2	Worthing	1	Mangotsfield United	0	
Round 2	Yeading	0	Billericay Town	4	
Replay	Altrincham	1	Gainsborough Trinity	0	
Replay	Eastwood Town	4	Bridlington Town	0	
Replay	Hayes	2	Tooting & Mitcham United	1	
Replay	Hornchurch	0	Cambridge City	4	
Replay	Hyde United	3	Kendal Town	2	
Replay	Oxford City	2	Tonbridge Angels	4	
Replay	St. Albans City	3	Cray Wanderers	2	(aet)
Round 3	Accrington Stanley	0	Hereford United	0	
Round 3	Barnet	1	Farnborough Town	0	
Round 3	Barrow	2	Scarborough	1	
Round 3	Bath City	0	Canvey Island	3	
Round 3	Billericay Town	2	Exeter City	2	
Round 3	Burton Albion	3	York City	0	
Round 3	Carlisle United	3	Redditch United	1	
Round 3	Crawley Town	3	Worthing	2	
Round 3	Dagenham & Redbridge	1	Bishop's Stortford	2	
Round 3	Eastwood Town	3	Spennymoor United	2	
Round 3	Forest Green Rovers	1	Aylesbury United	2	
Round 3	Gravesend & Northfleet	0	Eastbourne Borough	0	
Round 3	Halifax Town	0	Northwich Victoria	1	
Round 3	Hednesford Town	1	Worcester City	0	
Round 3	Hyde United	3	Whitby Town	3	
Round 3	Kettering Town	0	Alfreton Town	0	
Round 3	Leigh RMI	1	Altrincham	2	
Round 3	Leyton	0	Cheshunt	0	
Round 3	Morecambe	2	Sutton Coldfield Town	1	
Round 3	Redbridge	1	Cambridge City	5	
Round 3	Slough Town	4	Hendon	3	
Round 3	Southport	2	Hucknall Town	2	
Round 3	St. Albans City	0	Havant & Waterlooville	1	
Round 3	Stamford	3	Willenhall Town	1	
Round 3	Sutton United	0	Grays Athletic	2	
Round 3	Tamworth	5	Gresley Rovers	0	
Round 3	Team Bath	1	Histon	2	
Round 3	Thurrock	1	Aldershot Town	0	
Round 3	Tonbridge Angels	1	Walton & Hersham	1	
Round 3	Vauxhall Motors (Cheshire)	1	Lancaster City	1	
Round 3	Woking	1	Stevenage Borough	0	
Round 3	Yate Town	1	Hayes	1	
Replay	Alfreton Town	2	Kettering Town	1	
Replay	Cheshunt	0	Leyton	3	
Replay	Eastbourne Borough	0	Gravesend & Northfleet	1	
Replay	Exeter City	2	Billericay Town	0	
Replay	Hayes	7	Yate Town	2	
Replay	Hereford United	4	Accrington Stanley	0	
Replay	Hucknall Town	1	Southport	0	
Replay	Lancaster City	3	Vauxhall Motors (Cheshire)	0	

Replay	Walton & Hersham	1	Tonbridge Angels	1	(aet)
	Walton & Hersham won on penalties				
Replay	Whitby Town	0	Hyde United	1	
Round 4	Alfreton Town	0	Woking	3	
Round 4	Altrincham	1	Barrow	0	
Round 4	Aylesbury United	0	Canvey Island	1	
Round 4	Bishop's Stortford	3	Leyton	0	
Round 4	Burton Albion	2	Hednesford Town	0	
Round 4	Cambridge City	3	Crawley Town	3	
Round 4	Carlisle United	4	Barnet	1	
Round 4	Eastwood Town	1	Hayes	0	
Round 4	Gravesend & Northfleet	2	Histon	1	
Round 4	Grays Athletic	5	Havant & Waterlooville	0	
Round 4	Hereford United	3	Hyde United	0	
Round 4	Lancaster City	1	Morecambe	2	
Round 4	Northwich Victoria	0	Hucknall Town	1	
Round 4	Slough Town	1	Thurrock	0	
Round 4	Stamford	0	Walton & Hersham	0	
Round 4	Tamworth	0	Exeter City	3	
Replay	Walton & Hersham	3	Stamford	3	(aet)
	Stamford won on penalties				
Round 5	Altrincham	2	Grays Athletic	4	
Round 5	Burton Albion	1	Morecambe	0	
Round 5	Cambridge City	0	Hucknall Town	1	
Round 5	Canvey Island	2	Bishop's Stortford	2	
Round 5	Eastwood Town	1	Hereford United	1	
Round 5	Gravesend & Northfleet	3	Slough Town	2	
Round 5	Stamford	0	Exeter City	1	
Round 5	Woking	1	Carlisle United	0	
Replay	Bishop's Stortford	2	Canvey Island	1	
Replay	Hereford United	4	Eastwood Town	2	
Round 6	Bishop's Stortford	1	Gravesend & Northfleet	1	
Round 6	Burton Albion	1	Woking	0	
Round 6	Grays Athletic	4	Exeter City	1	
Round 6	Hereford United	2	Hucknall Town	2	
Replay	Gravesend & Northfleet	2	Bishop's Stortford	3	(aet)
Replay	Hucknall Town	1	Hereford United	0	

SEMI-FINALS

2nd leg	Hucknall Town	3	Bishop's Stortford	2	
1st leg	Bishop's Stortford	1	Hucknall Town	2	
	Hucknall Town won 5-3 on aggregate				
1st leg	Grays Athletic	5	Burton Albion	0	
2nd leg	Burton Albion	0	Grays Athletic	2	
	Grays Athletic won 7-0 on aggregate				

FINAL	Grays Athletic	1	Hucknall Town	1	(aet)
	Grays Athletic won on penalties				

F.A. Vase 2004/2005

Round 1	AFC Wallingford	0	AFC Newbury	7	
Round 1	Alvechurch	0	Buckingham Town	0	(aet)
Round 1	Amesbury Town	0	Bridgwater Town	3	
Round 1	Backwell United	2	Corsham Town	1	
Round 1	Barrow Town	2	Barnt Green Spartak	4	(aet)
Round 1	Barwell	0	Glossop North End	2	
Round 1	Blackwell MW	0	Holbeach United	2	(aet)
Round 1	Boston Town	5	Dudley Town	2	
Round 1	Brentwood	0	Harwich & Parkeston	2	
Round 1	Brislington	3	Bishop's Cleeve	0	
Round 1	Brockenhurst	0	Thamesmead Town	3	
Round 1	Burnham Ramblers	0	Harefield United	1	(aet)
Round 1	Bury Town	4	Leverstock Green	3	
Round 1	Carlton Town	4	Kirby Muxloe	1	
Round 1	Causeway United	2	Bridgnorth Town	0	
Round 1	Christchurch	4	Bemerton Heath Harlequins	0	
Round 1	Clacton Town	3	Newmarket Town	1	
Round 1	Clevedon Town	3	Slimbridge	6	(aet)
Round 1	Coventry Sphinx	1	Ludlow Town	1	(aet)
Round 1	Cowes Sports	2	Hungerford Town	1	
Round 1	Crook Town	1	Horden CW	2	
Round 1	Cullompton Rangers	0	Wimborne Town	4	
Round 1	Curzon Ashton	4	Washington	3	
Round 1	Dawlish Town	0	Bodmin Town	5	
Round 1	Deal Town	3	Petersfield Town	1	
Round 1	Didcot Town	1	Abingdon United	0	
Round 1	Durham City	3	Maltby Main	1	
Round 1	Eccleshill United	1	Esh Winning	4	
Round 1	Edgware Town	2	Waltham Abbey	1	
Round 1	Enfield	2	Halstead Town	1	
Round 1	Enfield Town	2	Diss Town	1	
Round 1	Epsom & Ewell	2	East Preston	3	
Round 1	Erith Town	3	BAT Sports	1	(aet)
Round 1	Eton Manor	2	March Town United	2	(aet)
Round 1	Fareham Town	3	Moneyfields	1	
Round 1	Flackwell Heath	2	London Colney	4	
Round 1	Frome Town	2	Hallen	0	
Round 1	Glapwell	1	Oldbury United	2	
Round 1	Greenwich Borough	3	Rye & Iden United	2	
Round 1	Guisborough Town	3	Bacup Borough	2	
Round 1	Hailsham Town	0	Three Bridges	3	
Round 1	Hanwell Town	3	Ilford	5	(aet)
Round 1	Hassocks	3	Witney United	4	
Round 1	Haverhill Rovers	2	Brook House	4	(aet)
Round 1	Hertford Town	2	Long Melford	3	(aet)
Round 1	Highgate United	2	Birstall United	0	
Round 1	Hoddesdon Town	2	Kirkley	3	(aet)
Round 1	Ipswich Wanderers	0	Sporting Bengal United	2	
Round 1	Jarrow Roofing Boldon CA	4	Morpeth Town	1	
Round 1	Kingsbury Town	4	Romford	3	(aet)
Round 1	Launceston	1	Welton Rovers	1	(aet)
	Launceston were disqualified for fielding an ineligible player				
Round 1	Ledbury Town	4	Biddulph Victoria	1	
Round 1	Liskeard Athletic	4	Street	3	

Round 1	Lordswood	1	Hillingdon Borough	2	
Round 1	Loughborough Dynamo	5	Harrowby United	3	
Round 1	Lowestoft Town	3	Witham Town	1	
Round 1	Lymington Town	3	Mile Oak	1	
Round 1	Maidstone United	4	Whitstable Town	1	
Round 1	Malvern Town	4	Staveley MW	1	
Round 1	Mickleover Sports	6	Kimberley Town	1	
Round 1	Mildenhall Town	6	Godmanchester Rovers	0	
Round 1	Milton United (Oxon)	2	Whitehawk	1	(aet)
Round 1	Newcastle Town	2	Buxton	0	
Round 1	North Greenford United	0	Stotfold	2	
Round 1	Oakwood	2	Alton Town	4	
Round 1	Pagham	1	Tunbridge Wells	3	
Round 1	Penrith	0	Salford City	2	
Round 1	Peterlee Newtown	1	Fleetwood Town	3	
Round 1	Pickering Town	2	Sheffield	1	
Round 1	Potters Bar Town	6	Whitton United	1	
Round 1	Prudhoe Town	0	Thackley	5	
Round 1	Quorn	3	Heanor Town	0	
Round 1	Rainworth MW	0	Friar Lane & Epworth	1	
Round 1	Ramsbottom United	3	Consett	0	
Round 1	Ramsgate	4	Chichester City United	1	
Round 1	Retford United	0	Cammell Laird	6	
Round 1	Ryton	1	Skelmersdale United	3	
Round 1	Sandhurst Town	1	Reading Town	0	
Round 1	Seaham Red Star	2	Selby Town	1	
Round 1	Shepton Mallet	0	Bournemouth	3	
Round 1	Shildon	0	Bedlington Terriers	1	
Round 1	Silsden	2	Tadcaster Albion	1	
Round 1	Slade Green	1	Abingdon Town	3	
Round 1	Soham Town Rangers	5	Royston Town	0	
Round 1	Southend Manor	1	Potton United	2	
Round 1	St Helens Town	6	Hallam	2	
Round 1	St Margaretsbury	0	Broxbourne Borough V&E	2	
Round 1	Stourbridge	4	Bourne Town	1	
Round 1	Sutton Town	3	Stratford Town	0	
Round 1	Thornaby	1	Great Harwood Town	0	
Round 1	Tipton Town	1	Holwell Sports	0	
Round 1	Tiptree United	2	Sawbridgeworth Town	2	(aet)
Round 1	Wellington Town	1	Chipping Norton Town	2	
Round 1	Westbury United	1	Exmouth Town	3	(aet)
Round 1	Westfields	1	Long Eaton United	2	
Round 1	Whickham	0	Dunston Federation Brewery	2	
Round 1	Whitley Bay	3	Newcastle Blue Star	1	
Round 1	Wick	1	VCD Athletic	4	(aet)
Round 1	Willand Rovers	4	Devizes Town	4	(aet)
Round 1	Woodford United	2	Stansted	1	
Round 1	Yorkshire Amateur	2	Marske United	0	
Replay	Buckingham Town	2	Alvechurch	4	
Replay	Devizes Town	2	Willand Rovers	1	
Replay	Ludlow Town	0	Coventry Sphinx	4	
Replay	March Town United	1	Eton Manor	1	(aet)
	Eton Manor won on penalties				
Replay	Sawbridgeworth Town	2	Tiptree United	1	
Round 2	AFC Newbury	2	North Leigh	1	
Round 2	Alton Town	2	Winchester City	6	

Round 2	Andover	0	Fareham Town	1	
Round 2	Backwell United	4	Wimborne Town	0	
Round 2	Barnt Green Spartak	0	Studley	4	
Round 2	Bedlington Terriers	1	Silsden	0	
Round 2	Bideford	0	Bodmin Town	1	
Round 2	Bitton	3	Christchurch	3	(aet)
Round 2	Boston Town	0	Mickleover Sports	1	
Round 2	Bournemouth	1	Lymington & New Milton	3	
Round 2	Bridgwater Town	3	Liskeard Athletic	3	(aet)
Round 2	Brislington	3	Torrington	0	
Round 2	Brook House	2	Sawbridgeworth Town	1	
Round 2	Carlton Town	0	Desborough Town	3	
Round 2	Clacton Town	1	Harefield United	1	(aet)
Round 2	Colne	5	Congleton Town	0	
Round 2	Cowes Sports	1	Hillingdon Borough	2	
Round 2	Curzon Ashton	2	Guisborough Town	3	
Round 2	Deal Town	1	Witney United	0	
Round 2	Dunston Federation Brewery	2	Pickering Town	4	
Round 2	East Preston	0	Didcot Town	4	
Round 2	Edgware Town	1	Potton United	4	
Round 2	Enfield	5	Concord Rangers	0	
Round 2	Enfield Town	2	London Colney	0	
Round 2	Esh Winning	1	West Allotment Celtic	2	
Round 2	Fleetwood Town	2	St Helens Town	3	
Round 2	Frome Town	3	Devizes Town	1	
Round 2	Gedling Town	3	Nantwich Town	0	
Round 2	Gosport Borough	3	VCD Athletic	2	(aet)
Round 2	Holbeach United	2	Alvechurch	1	(aet)
Round 2	Horden CW	1	Salford City	2	
Round 2	Ilford	1	Bury Town	2	
Round 2	Jarrow Roofing Boldon CA	3	Cammell Laird	1	
Round 2	Kingsbury Town	3	Broxbourne Borough V&E	2	
Round 2	Ledbury Town	2	Sutton Town	0	
Round 2	Long Melford	3	Harwich & Parkeston	2	
Round 2	Loughborough Dynamo	1	Leamington	1	(aet)
Round 2	Lowestoft Town	3	Mildenhall Town	2	
Round 2	Lymington Town	0	Abingdon Town	1	
Round 2	Malvern Town	4	Coventry Sphinx	3	(aet)
Round 2	Oadby Town	3	Long Eaton United	1	
Round 2	Oldbury United	3	Friar Lane & Epworth	0	
Round 2	Quorn	1	Glossop North End	1	(aet)
Round 2	Ramsgate	2	Greenwich Borough	2	(aet)
Round 2	Sandhurst Town	3	Milton United (Oxon)	1	
Round 2	Seaham Red Star	2	Durham City	4	
Round 2	Skelmersdale United	3	Ramsbottom United	0	
Round 2	Slimbridge	4	Chipping Norton Town	0	
Round 2	Soham Town Rangers	5	Sporting Bengal United	1	
Round 2	St Blazey	6	Keynsham Town	0	
Round 2	St Neots Town	3	Potters Bar Town	2	
Round 2	Stone Dominoes	3	Causeway United	2	
Round 2	Stotfold	0	AFC Sudbury	1	
Round 2	Stourbridge	5	Highgate United	0	
Round 2	Thackley	3	Whitley Bay	1	
Round 2	Thamesmead Town	2	Maidstone United	1	
Round 2	Thornaby	0	Billingham Town	2	
Round 2	Three Bridges	4	Chertsey Town	4	(aet)
Round 2	Tipton Town	2	Newcastle Town	1	

Round 2	Tunbridge Wells	4	Erith Town	3	
Round 2	Welton Rovers	1	Exmouth Town	2	
Round 2	Woodford United	2	Eton Manor	0	
Round 2	Wroxham	4	Kirkley	2	
Round 2	Yorkshire Amateur	3	Billingham Synthonia	3	(aet)
Replay	Billingham Synthonia	4	Yorkshire Amateur	0	
Replay	Chertsey Town	2	Three Bridges	1	
Replay	Christchurch	0	Bitton	1	
Replay	Glossop North End	1	Quorn	3	
Replay	Greenwich Borough	0	Ramsgate	2	
Replay	Harefield United	3	Clacton Town	1	
Replay	Leamington	3	Loughborough Dynamo	0	
Replay	Liskeard Athletic	1	Bridgwater Town	4	
Round 3	AFC Newbury	2	Sandhurst Town	0	
Round 3	Abingdon Town	0	Desborough Town	2	
Round 3	Backwell United	2	Slimbridge	1	(aet)
Round 3	Billingham Synthonia	2	Pickering Town	3	(aet)
Round 3	Billingham Town	4	St Helens Town	3	
Round 3	Bitton	2	Ramsgate	0	
Round 3	Bodmin Town	5	Hillingdon Borough	1	
Round 3	Bridgwater Town	2	Exmouth Town	1	
Round 3	Brislington	1	Woodford United	0	
Round 3	Bury Town	1	Tunbridge Wells	0	
Round 3	Colne	1	Stone Dominoes	1	(aet)
Round 3	Deal Town	1	Fareham Town	0	(aet)
Round 3	Enfield	1	Enfield Town	0	
Round 3	Gosport Borough	0	Didcot Town	1	
Round 3	Guisborough Town	1	Jarrow Roofing Boldon CA	2	
Round 3	Harefield United	1	AFC Sudbury	3	
Round 3	Holbeach United	2	Thackley	4	
Round 3	Kingsbury Town	1	Frome Town	2	
Round 3	Leamington	2	Bedlington Terriers	3	(aet)
Round 3	Ledbury Town	3	Studley	1	
Round 3	Long Melford	0	Brook House	0	(aet)
Round 3	Lowestoft Town	5	Chertsey Town	1	
Round 3	Lymington & New Milton	4	Wroxham	1	
Round 3	Malvern Town	1	Skelmersdale United	3	
Round 3	Oldbury United	1	Gedling Town	2	
Round 3	Potton United	2	St Blazey	1	
Round 3	Quorn	2	Mickleover Sports	1	
Round 3	Salford City	1	West Allotment Celtic	2	
Round 3	St Neots Town	3	Soham Town Rangers	4	
Round 3	Stourbridge	1	Oadby Town	0	
Round 3	Thamesmead Town	1	Winchester City	3	
Round 3	Tipton Town	2	Durham City	1	
Replay	Brook House	3	Long Melford	0	
Replay	Stone Dominoes	0	Colne	1	
Round 4	AFC Newbury	1	Thackley	0	
Round 4	Backwell United	0	Lowestoft Town	0	(aet)
Round 4	Billingham Town	1	Lymington & New Milton	3	
Round 4	Bitton	1	Bedlington Terriers	2	
Round 4	Bodmin Town	2	Colne	3	
Round 4	Bridgwater Town	2	Winchester City	0	
Round 4	Bury Town	2	Potton United	1	
Round 4	Didcot Town	2	Ledbury Town	0	

Round 4	Enfield	1	Brislington	0	
Round 4	Jarrow Roofing Boldon CA	3	Deal Town	0	
Round 4	Pickering Town	1	Brook House	3	(aet)
Round 4	Quorn	2	AFC Sudbury	3	(aet)
Round 4	Skelmersdale United	0	Frome Town	2	
Round 4	Stourbridge	1	Desborough Town	0	
Round 4	Tipton Town	3	Gedling Town	0	
Round 4	West Allotment Celtic	1	Soham Town Rangers	3	
Replay	Lowestoft Town	0	Backwell United	3	
Round 5	Backwell United	1	Stourbridge	2	
Round 5	Bridgwater Town	0	AFC Sudbury	4	
Round 5	Bury Town	3	Lymington & New Milton	2	(aet)
Round 5	Colne	2	Didcot Town	3	
Round 5	Enfield	0	Bedlington Terriers	3	
Round 5	Frome Town	3	Brook House	0	
Round 5	Jarrow Roofing Boldon CA	1	Tipton Town	1	(aet)
Round 5	Soham Town Rangers	0	AFC Newbury	1	
Replay	Tipton Town	1	Jarrow Roofing Boldon CA	1	(aet)
	Jarrow Roofing Boldon CA won on penalties				
Round 6	AFC Sudbury	4	Stourbridge	1	(aet)
Round 6	Bedlington Terriers	2	AFC Newbury	1	
Round 6	Didcot Town	2	Bury Town	1	
Round 6	Jarrow Roofing Boldon CA	3	Frome Town	0	

SEMI-FINALS

1st leg	AFC Sudbury	2	Bedlington Terriers	1	
2nd leg	Bedlington Terriers	2	AFC Sudbury	1	(aet)
	Aggregate score 3-3. AFC Sudbury won on penalties				
1st leg	Didcot Town	1	Jarrow Roofing Boldon CA	0	
2nd leg	Jarrow Roofing Boldon CA	0	Didcot Town	1	
	Didcot Town won 2-0 on aggregate				
FINAL	Didcot Town	3	AFC Sudbury	2	

Nationwide Conference National Fixtures 2005/2006	Accrington Stanley	Aldershot Town	Altrincham	Burton Albion	Cambridge United	Canvey Island	Crawley Town	Dagenham & Redbridge	Exeter City	Forest Green Rovers	Gravesend & Northfleet	Grays Athletic	Halifax Town	Hereford United	Kidderminster Harriers	Morecambe	Scarborough	Southport	Stevenage Borough	Tamworth	Woking	York City
AccringtonStanley	■	20/09	24/01	25/02	21/01	13/08	17/09	11/02	27/08	19/11	01/10	01/04	02/01	08/10	10/12	21/02	17/04	26/11	18/03	22/04	03/09	29/10
Aldershot Town	04/02	■	27/08	18/02	08/04	24/01	05/09	11/03	02/01	26/11	29/10	17/04	21/01	27/09	15/10	25/02	25/03	10/12	17/09	13/08	22/04	24/09
Altrincham	16/08	28/01	■	25/03	11/02	11/03	01/10	10/09	29/10	20/08	08/04	22/04	21/02	15/04	02/01	29/08	20/09	15/10	07/01	26/11	10/12	04/03
Burton Albion	10/09	01/10	29/10	■	21/02	27/08	19/11	04/03	11/02	22/04	10/12	13/08	24/01	18/03	26/11	20/09	03/09	17/04	08/10	02/01	21/01	01/04
Cambridge United	20/08	19/11	24/09	27/09	■	31/12	29/10	29/04	25/02	07/01	28/01	04/02	18/03	16/08	29/08	01/04	03/12	18/02	26/12	08/10	17/09	15/04
Canvey Island	07/01	16/08	08/10	28/01	26/11	■	25/02	29/08	22/04	01/04	20/08	02/01	10/12	18/02	15/04	29/10	17/09	24/09	27/09	19/11	04/02	18/03
Crawley Town	04/03	15/04	18/02	08/04	25/03	10/09	■	16/08	15/10	04/02	26/11	24/09	22/04	20/08	27/09	28/01	11/03	29/10	29/08	10/12	02/01	07/01
Dagenham & Red.	24/09	08/10	25/02	17/09	10/12	17/04	24/01	■	03/09	29/10	02/01	27/09	01/04	19/11	22/04	18/03	27/08	13/08	18/02	21/01	26/11	04/02
Exeter City	28/01	26/12	01/04	24/09	10/09	03/12	18/03	15/04	■	29/08	07/01	19/11	08/10	31/12	16/08	20/08	29/04	04/03	04/02	29/10	27/09	18/02
Forest Green Rovers	08/04	31/12	21/01	03/12	13/08	29/10	20/09	25/03	17/04	■	21/02	03/09	27/08	26/12	04/03	01/10	11/02	11/03	29/04	24/01	15/10	10/09
Gravesend & North.	18/02	01/04	19/11	29/04	27/08	21/01	31/12	26/12	13/08	27/09	■	24/01	17/09	04/02	24/09	03/12	25/02	03/09	29/10	18/03	17/04	08/10
Grays Athletic	29/10	29/08	03/12	07/01	20/09	26/12	11/02	21/02	08/04	15/04	16/08	■	01/10	28/01	10/09	29/04	15/10	25/03	31/12	04/03	11/03	20/08
Halifax Town	26/12	20/08	27/09	16/08	15/10	29/04	03/12	29/10	11/03	28/01	04/03	18/02	■	24/09	04/02	07/01	31/12	08/04	15/04	10/09	25/03	29/08
Hereford United	11/03	21/02	03/09	15/10	24/01	01/10	21/01	08/04	26/11	02/01	20/09	27/08	11/02	■	25/03	17/09	13/08	22/04	25/02	17/04	29/10	10/12
Kidderminster Harr.	29/04	18/03	26/12	31/12	17/04	03/09	21/02	03/12	24/01	17/09	11/02	25/02	20/09	29/10	■	08/10	21/01	27/08	01/04	01/10	13/08	19/11
Morecambe	27/09	10/09	17/04	04/02	29/10	25/03	27/08	15/10	21/01	18/02	22/04	10/12	13/08	04/03	11/03	■	24/01	02/01	24/09	03/09	08/04	26/11
Scarborough	29/08	29/10	04/02	15/04	22/04	04/03	08/10	28/01	10/12	24/09	10/09	18/03	26/11	07/01	20/08	16/08	■	27/09	19/11	01/04	18/02	02/01
Southport	31/12	29/04	18/03	29/08	01/10	11/02	01/04	07/01	17/09	08/10	15/04	29/10	19/11	03/12	28/01	26/12	21/02	■	20/08	20/09	25/02	16/08
Stevenage Borough	15/10	04/03	13/08	11/03	02/01	21/02	17/04	01/10	20/09	10/12	25/03	26/11	03/09	10/09	29/10	11/02	08/04	21/01	■	27/08	24/01	22/04
Tamworth	03/12	07/01	31/12	26/12	11/03	08/04	29/04	20/08	25/03	16/08	15/10	17/09	25/02	29/08	18/02	15/04	29/10	04/02	28/01	■	24/09	27/09
Woking	15/04	03/12	29/04	20/08	04/03	20/09	26/12	31/12	21/02	18/03	29/08	08/10	29/10	01/04	07/01	19/11	01/10	10/09	16/08	11/02	■	28/01
York City	25/03	11/02	17/09	29/10	03/09	15/10	13/08	20/09	01/10	25/02	11/03	21/01	17/04	29/04	08/04	31/12	26/12	24/01	03/12	21/02	27/08	■

Nationwide Conference North Fixtures 2005/2006	Alfreton Town	Barrow	Droylsden	Gainsborough Trinity	Harrogate Town	Hednesford Town	Hinckley United	Hucknall Town	Hyde United	Kettering Town	Lancaster City	Leigh RMI	Moor Green	Northwich Victoria	Nuneaton Borough	Redditch United	Stafford Rangers	Stalybridge Celtic	Vauxhall Motors	Worcester City	Workington	Worksop Town
Alfreton Town		18/02	04/02	29/04	05/11	14/01	04/03	26/12	17/04	08/11	03/09	18/10	25/03	27/08	08/04	10/09	11/03	15/10	13/08	19/11	31/12	21/01
Barrow	22/10		25/02	11/02	21/02	13/08	01/10	17/04	03/09	08/04	02/01	27/08	05/11	21/01	22/04	10/12	19/11	17/09	14/01	11/03	08/11	25/03
Droylsden	01/10	10/09		22/10	25/03	31/12	11/02	03/09	20/02	11/03	08/04	14/01	21/01	26/12	13/08	04/03	05/11	29/04	27/08	17/04	19/11	07/11
Gainsborough Trinity	10/12	15/10	18/02		08/11	27/08	10/09	25/03	04/03	22/04	19/11	03/09	13/08	14/01	05/11	04/02	08/04	18/10	17/04	21/01	11/03	02/01
Harrogate Town	18/03	18/10	12/11	07/03		01/04	29/10	14/01	13/08	17/09	22/04	02/01	27/08	03/12	21/01	18/02	10/12	04/02	15/10	03/09	25/02	17/04
Hednesford Town	15/08	07/01	22/04	28/01	19/11		20/08	07/11	08/04	22/10	05/11	04/03	20/02	10/09	02/01	15/04	01/10	29/08	10/12	25/03	11/02	11/03
Hinckley United	17/09	04/02	15/10	25/02	11/03	21/01		27/08	19/11	02/01	13/08	17/04	08/11	03/09	10/12	18/10	25/03	18/02	22/04	14/01	05/11	08/04
Hucknall Town	02/01	29/08	15/04	12/11	16/08	07/03	28/01		22/10	21/02	10/12	22/04	01/10	29/10	17/09	03/12	07/01	01/04	18/03	25/02	20/08	11/02
Hyde United	29/08	15/04	17/10	17/09	07/01	03/12	01/04	18/02		28/01	15/10	12/11	29/04	18/03	04/02	29/10	20/08	26/12	06/03	31/12	15/08	25/02
Kettering Town	07/03	03/12	29/10	31/12	04/03	18/02	26/12	18/10	27/08		21/01	15/10	14/01	04/02	17/04	18/03	10/09	12/11	01/04	13/08	29/04	03/09
Lancaster City	15/04	26/12	03/12	01/04	31/12	18/03	07/01	29/04	11/02	20/08		07/03	22/10	12/11	25/02	28/01	29/08	16/08	29/10	01/10	21/02	17/09
Leigh RMI	21/02	28/01	16/08	15/04	26/12	17/09	29/08	31/12	25/03	11/02	08/11		11/03	29/04	19/11	07/01	22/10	20/08	25/02	08/04	01/10	05/11
Moor Green	12/11	18/03	20/08	07/01	28/01	18/10	07/03	04/02	10/12	16/08	18/02	29/10		01/04	15/10	02/01	15/04	25/02	03/12	17/09	29/08	22/04
Northwich Victoria	28/01	20/08	02/01	16/08	08/04	25/02	15/04	11/03	05/11	01/10	25/03	10/12	19/11		08/11	29/08	22/04	07/01	17/09	11/02	22/10	21/02
Nuneaton Borough	03/12	31/12	07/01	18/03	20/08	26/12	29/04	04/03	01/10	29/08	10/09	01/04	11/02	07/03		16/08	28/01	29/10	12/11	21/02	15/04	22/10
Redditch United	25/02	29/04	17/09	01/10	22/10	03/09	21/02	08/04	11/03	05/11	27/08	13/08	26/12	17/04	14/01		11/02	31/12	21/01	08/11	25/03	19/11
Stafford Rangers	29/10	01/04	18/03	03/12	29/04	04/02	12/11	13/08	21/01	25/02	17/04	18/02	03/09	31/12	27/08	15/10		07/03	18/10	26/12	17/09	14/01
Stalybridge Celtic	11/02	04/03	10/12	21/02	01/10	17/04	22/10	19/11	02/01	25/03	14/01	21/01	10/09	13/08	11/03	22/04	08/11		03/09	05/11	08/04	27/08
Vauxhall Motors	07/01	16/08	28/01	29/08	11/02	29/04	31/12	05/11	08/11	19/11	11/03	10/09	08/04	04/03	25/03	20/08	21/02	15/04		22/10	26/12	01/10
Worcester City	01/04	29/10	29/08	20/08	15/04	12/11	15/08	10/09	22/04	07/01	04/02	03/12	04/03	15/10	17/10	06/03	02/01	18/03	18/02		28/01	10/12
Workington	22/04	07/03	01/04	29/10	10/09	15/10	18/03	21/01	14/01	10/12	18/10	04/02	17/04	18/02	03/09	12/11	04/03	03/12	02/01	27/08		13/08
Worksop Town	20/08	12/11	07/03	26/12	29/08	29/10	03/12	15/10	10/09	15/04	04/03	18/03	31/12	18/10	18/02	01/04	16/08	28/01	04/02	29/04	07/01	

Nationwide Conference South Fixtures 2005/2006	Basingstoke Town	Bishop's Stortford	Bognor Regis Town	Cambridge City	Carshalton Athletic	Dorchester Town	Eastbourne Borough	Eastleigh	Farnborough Town	Havant & Waterlooville	Hayes	Histon	Lewes	Maidenhead United	Newport County	St. Albans City	Sutton United	Thurrock	Welling United	Weston-super-Mare	Weymouth	Yeading
Basingstoke Town		11/02	10/12	25/02	29/08	13/08	21/01	02/01	17/09	21/02	22/04	17/04	11/03	08/04	29/10	27/08	17/09	25/03	22/10	14/01	08/11	19/11
Bishop's Stortford	15/10		18/02	04/02	14/01	21/01	13/08	17/04	29/08	19/11	25/02	08/11	29/10	18/10	25/03	02/01	17/09	11/03	10/12	27/08	22/04	08/04
Bognor Regis Town	29/04	22/10		17/09	17/04	14/01	27/08	29/08	29/10	26/12	11/02	25/03	21/02	08/11	11/03	21/01	25/02	19/11	17/09	31/12	08/04	13/08
Cambridge City	10/09	17/09	04/03		08/04	27/08	29/08	19/11	10/12	11/03	21/02	02/01	25/03	21/01	22/04	14/01	22/10	08/11	11/02	13/08	29/10	17/04
Carshalton Athletic	15/04	16/08	29/08	03/12		01/04	07/03	11/02	25/02	22/10	12/11	17/09	20/08	17/09	07/01	29/10	26/12	31/12	21/02	18/03	28/01	29/04
Dorchester Town	07/01	20/08	16/08	28/01	19/11		10/12	08/04	25/03	08/11	17/09	22/04	22/10	29/10	21/02	17/09	29/08	11/02	15/04	25/02	02/01	11/03
Eastbourne Borough	20/08	07/01	28/01	15/04	08/11	29/04		11/03	08/04	25/03	22/10	19/11	26/12	31/12	17/09	25/02	21/02	16/08	29/08	17/09	11/02	29/10
Eastleigh	26/12	29/08	15/04	01/04	15/10	03/12	29/10		19/10	29/04	07/01	04/03	31/12	18/02	20/08	18/03	12/11	28/01	10/09	08/03	17/08	04/02
Farnborough Town	04/03	15/04	18/03	29/04	10/09	12/11	03/12	21/02		17/09	16/08	11/02	07/01	26/12	29/08	01/04	28/01	20/08	07/03	29/10	22/10	31/12
Havant & Waterloo.	17/09	01/04	02/01	29/10	18/02	06/03	12/11	10/12	04/02		20/08	10/09	29/08	15/10	28/01	22/04	15/08	15/04	18/03	03/12	07/01	04/03
Hayes	31/12	10/09	15/10	18/10	25/03	04/02	18/02	13/08	14/01	21/01		11/03	08/04	27/08	08/11	29/08	29/04	29/10	04/03	17/04	19/11	26/12
Histon	29/08	07/03	12/11	26/12	04/02	31/12	01/04	17/09	15/10	25/02	29/10		28/01	29/04	15/04	03/12	18/03	07/01	16/08	18/02	20/08	18/10
Lewes	29/10	18/03	19/10	12/11	21/01	18/02	02/01	22/04	13/08	17/04	03/12	27/08		29/08	10/09	04/02	08/03	04/03	01/04	15/10	10/12	14/01
Maidenhead United	03/12	21/02	07/03	20/08	04/03	18/03	22/04	22/10	02/01	11/02	28/01	10/12	15/04		16/08	12/11	07/01	29/08	29/10	01/04	17/09	10/09
Newport County	18/03	12/11	29/10	31/12	13/08	19/10	04/02	21/01	17/04	27/08	08/03	29/08	25/02	14/01		18/02	01/04	29/04	03/12	26/12	17/09	15/10
St. Albans City	28/01	26/12	20/08	16/08	11/03	04/03	10/09	29/10	19/11	31/12	15/04	08/04	17/09	25/03	22/10		11/02	21/02	07/01	29/04	29/08	08/11
Sutton United	04/02	04/03	10/09	18/02	02/01	17/04	18/10	25/03	27/08	14/01	10/12	29/10	08/11	13/08	19/11	15/10		08/04	22/04	29/08	11/03	21/01
Thurrock	12/11	29/10	01/04	06/03	22/04	15/10	14/01	27/08	21/01	29/08	18/03	13/08	17/09	17/04	10/12	17/10	03/12		02/01	04/02	25/02	18/02
Welling United	18/02	29/04	04/02	15/10	18/10	29/08	17/04	25/02	08/11	29/10	17/09	14/01	19/11	11/03	08/04	13/08	31/12	26/12		21/01	25/03	27/08
Weston-super-Mare	17/08	28/01	22/04	07/01	29/10	10/09	04/03	09/11	11/03	08/04	29/08	22/10	11/02	19/11	02/01	10/12	15/04	17/09	20/08		22/02	25/03
Weymouth	07/03	31/12	03/12	18/03	27/08	26/12	15/10	14/01	18/02	13/08	01/04	21/01	29/04	04/02	04/03	17/04	29/10	10/09	12/11	18/10		29/08
Yeading	01/04	03/12	07/01	29/08	10/12	29/10	18/03	17/09	22/04	17/09	02/01	21/02	16/08	25/02	11/02	07/03	20/08	22/10	28/01	12/11	15/04	

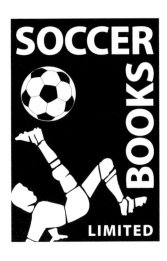

Supporters' Guide Series

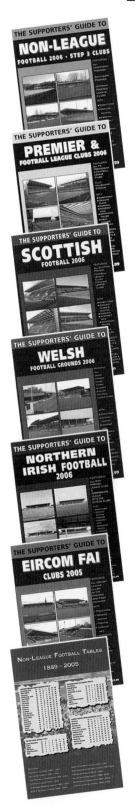

This top-selling series has been published annually since 1982 and contains 2004/2005 Season's results and tables, Directions, Photographs, Phone numbers, Parking information, Admission details, Disabled information and much more.

THE SUPPORTERS' GUIDE TO NON-LEAGUE FOOTBALL 2006 – STEP 3 CLUBS

Following the reorganisation of Non-League Football the 2nd edition of this book features the 66 clubs which feed into the Football Conference. *Price £6.99*

THE SUPPORTERS' GUIDE TO PREMIER & FOOTBALL LEAGUE CLUBS 2006

The 22nd edition features all Premiership and Football League clubs. *Price £6.99*

THE SUPPORTERS' GUIDE TO SCOTTISH FOOTBALL 2006

The 14th edition featuring all Scottish Premier League, Scottish League and Highland League clubs. *Price £6.99*

THE SUPPORTERS' GUIDE TO WELSH FOOTBALL GROUNDS 2006

The 10th edition featuring all League of Wales, Cymru Alliance & Welsh Football League Clubs + results, tables & much more. *Price £6.99*

THE SUPPORTERS' GUIDE TO NORTHERN IRISH FOOTBALL 2006

Back after a long absence, this 3rd edition features all Irish Premier League and Irish Football League Clubs + results, tables & much more. *Price £6.99*

THE SUPPORTERS' GUIDE TO EIRCOM FAI CLUBS 2005

Back after a long absence this 3rd edition features all Eircom League Premier and First Division Clubs + 10 years of results, tables & much more. *Price £6.99*

NON-LEAGUE FOOTBALL TABLES 1889-2005

The 4th edition contains final tables for the Conference, it's 3 feeder Leagues and also the Birmingham Combination, the Birmingham League, the Midland Football Alliance and the Shropshire & District League. *Price £9.95*

These books are available UK & Surface post free from –

Soccer Books Limited (Dept. SBL)
72 St. Peter's Avenue
Cleethorpes, N.E. Lincolnshire
DN35 8HU